The Girl Guide Annual

Published by special arrangement with
THE GIRL GUIDES ASSOCIATION

Edited by ROBERT MOSS

Purnell

The late Lady Baden-Powell, World Chief Guide, looks at the bronze sculpture of the Founder of Guides and Scouts, Lord Baden-Powell, at the Scout Association's Adult Training Centre, Gilwell Park, Essex

The World Badge

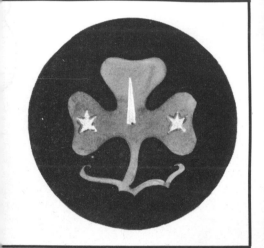

CHIEF SCOUT OF THE WORLD

Photo by Lawrence D. Curtis

What is Guiding?

by Anne Parker

It's a club for girls from ten to sixteen,
Considered by many the best that there's been;
It's wearing a uniform, smart and attractive;
It's leading a life that is healthy and active.
It's giving service to others in need,
Controlling oneself in thought, word and deed.
It's camping, exploring, in rain, hail or sun;
It's full of adventure, it's bursting with fun.
It's working together in one's own Patrol,
And smiling through hardship when spirits fall.
It's lasted through peacetime; it's lasted through war;
Its membership numbers six million or more.
It's making a Promise, a standard for living;
It's sharing and caring; it's loving and giving.
It's doing one's duty to God, Queen and nation
To the best that one can whatever one's station.
The members assemble in different headquarters,
In mud huts or skyscrapers, across many waters,
In igloos, log cabins and palaces royal,
Each doing her best to be honest and loyal.
It's a life full of promise, with adventure unfurled;
It's a family that's spread all over the world.

Who Were the Kidnappers?

by David Harwood

The Editor of the *Girl Guide Annual* and the *Brownie Annual* lives in a lane called Kidnappers' Lane. Who were the kidnappers that gave the lane its exciting, rather sinister, name? One answer given to inquiries associated the lane with the press gangs of the Napoleonic wars who kidnapped young, able-bodied men and pressed them into service with the Royal Navy. But the true explanation proved to be much less romantic. The lane was named from the napping of kids—baby goats—that was once carried on in it. The soft, short fibres were removed from the kids' coats in much the same way as the fleece is sheared from the backs of sheep.

Discovering the origin of local place-names is an interesting pursuit for Guides. Wherever you live, whether it's in the centre of a city, in the suburb of a town, or deep in the heart of the country, you'll come across curious place-names. Some may be recorded on large-scale maps, others you will come across by keeping your eyes open.

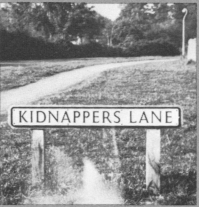

There are two main lines of investigation that will help you in your researches. There is your local public library. Not only is it likely to have a guide-book that may explain the origin of a local place-name, but there may well be other local publications that will give clues.

There may be a historical society that will provide a wealth of information about your locality. The librarian will be able to tell you whether there is one.

Older members of the community are another source of local information. A place-name might have originated during their lifetime, or they may have been told something about it by their parents or grandparents.

As a start, find out the origin of the name of your own village, town or district. In one of the photographs on this page is the name of the village of Broughton Gifford. Broughton comes from the Saxon word *Brookton*. *Brook* is a stream, and *ton* means *a dwelling.* Brookton was therefore *a dwelling by a brook.* The lords of the manor between 1260 and 1320 were called Gifford, and they added their name to Broughton, making it Broughton Gifford.

A number of villages in England have a "pound", which was where stray animals were impounded, or confined, in earlier times. Your own street may bear an interesting name. Find out the origin of it. Mill Lane was obviously named from the mill that once stood there, but the origin of other place-names may not be so easily traced.

It is fun to go in quest of origins.

Photographs by David Harwood and Robert Moss

Adventure for Patrols

by Jean Howard

Hunt for fossils, study rocks, discover the secrets of an old wall, explore the contents of a stream or pond, find an unusual wildflower.

To explore for rocks and fossils, each Guide will need a knapsack, a hammer, polythene bags for the samples found, a pencil and labels to mark them with and to record where they were found, and sunglasses or goggles for protection against flying splinters of rock. If you go far afield, take a map, a compass and a whistle.

Find a quarry or gorge or rocky outcrop, or, if you are by the sea, go to the foot of cliffs and you will see how layer after layer of sediment and rock has been built up by the forces of Nature during the millions of years of the earth's history. The layers are made up of different types of rock, some very hard and old, some softer and lighter in colour. Collect small pieces of the different types and put them in your knapsacks for studying later. Look for rocks and stones of strange shapes and sizes and colours and make a special note of imprints like the skeleton of a fish or other sea-creature. These could well be fossils, and from their shape you could get a good idea of what these living things were like thousands of years ago. Your Patrol might find something exciting that fits into the jigsaw puzzle of our past.

It is fascinating to study the life of an overgrown pond or stream

Secrets in an Old Wall

An old wall of mellow red brick may not sound very exciting at first, but interesting living things can be found in it.

A notebook and pencil are all that each Guide needs. You will be surprised at the long list of discoveries you have made at the end of an hour or two. All sorts of tiny plants and creepers and ferns will be there: lichens and mosses on the shady side, and, on the sunwarmed brick, tiny wildflower plants, struggling to survive; these may have grown

Photo: N. Scott

Photo: Robert D. Bristow

How exciting to come across an old foot-and-horse bridge crossing a meadow or a disused canal!

from seeds blown by the wind into crevices or dropped by passing birds. Sometimes on the top of the wall where soil has collected there may be a cascade of ivy or gay valerian.

Not only will you find plant life but insects: spiders that have made their nests there, ladybirds and beetles, caterpillars the colour of the leaves they are resting on, and moths hiding in the cracks until darkness falls. Butterflies and bees pay hurried visits to the flowers on the wall, and ants march up and down like regiments of soldiers. Even a nervous mouse may be seen scurrying along through the nettles at the bottom of the wall.

In the Pond

You will probably not need to go very far to find a pond or a small stagnant stream or ditch, where the still water is half overgrown with various forms of pond-weed. Here flowers and grasses grow abundantly.

You might discover an old, overgrown culvert like this one carrying a waterway under a road

It is fascinating to study pond-life. You may find dandelions with huge heads, thistles, water-iris, meadowsweet, purple loosestrife, buttercups, and ragwort with a host of brown furry caterpillars. You will be amazed how many different varieties you will find. Don't be tempted to taste the deadly nightshade with its luscious-looking poisonous berries if you come across it.

The water in the pond may look dull and lifeless, except for the water-boatmen darting endlessly to and fro, but just dip a jamjar in and see how many tiny creatures there are in the murky water: tadpoles perhaps, tiny fish, worms, snails and many other "wiggly things". Keep a note of them all and learn about them.

There are the living things on the banks too. A little green frog may suddenly leap from under your feet and dive into the pond for safety. A brilliant dragonfly may skim over the water, turning and swooping down on its prey, and then, in a flash of colour, be gone. Unheeding, hardworking bees continue to gather the nectar from the clover.

Ladybirds and beetles, moths and many kinds of butterfly will be around the pond. Search carefully and quietly, and your list of "finds" will grow longer and longer. Perhaps when you have found many of the wonderful things there are in the pond you will want to turn the Patrol into a working party to rid it of its clutter of tins, old tyres, wire, broken glass, pram and cycle parts, etc., and restore it to its original beauty.

Twig Art

Morning Stroller

Ballet Dancer

Exploring the Arts? Then here's something fresh and original that you might enjoy taking up.

On Nature hikes search about for sticks and twigs of shapes that could suggest human figures walking, gesturing, dancing, leaping.

By pruning here and there you may be able to turn an ordinary stick or twig into a shape that conveys an impression of joyousness, vigour, eeriness, or even horror.

The photographs on these pages will give you an idea of what can be done with a little imagination.

8

Photos by Alan T. Band Associates

Twig Men

**High Jumper or Joy
of Spring**

**Abominable Snowman or Ghoul or Horror From
Outer Space**

9

Hiker

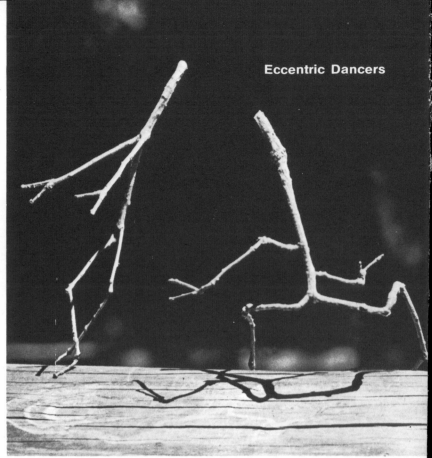

Eccentric Dancers

Witches

The Water Sprite

by Jean Howard

Helma strapped on her skis, and, waving to her mother, pushed off down the steep valley towards the village of Lilledal below.

It was Saturday morning and she was on her way to her Guide meeting with her friend Magda, who lived farther down the hillside. In summer these were lush green pastures full of wildflowers, with cattle grazing quietly; but now, in December, all was frozen and white and the fir-trees in the forest behind Magda's home were spangled with heavy frost.

With a quick turn on her skis, Helma stopped at the door, and Magda came out smiling. "I'm all ready, but we must stop at Frue Olsen's on the way as I've got a cake for her birthday and some wool for a new shawl. She has so few visitors, and she likes to have some knitting to pass the time in the long dark evenings."

The two Guides set off to race each other down the snowy slope. The air was cold in spite of the winter sunshine that made the snow on the high mountain-tops sparkle against the blue sky.

It was a beautiful day, and they soon reached the little wooden house. The old lady was delighted with her gifts. She was very excited because her daugh-ter and grandchild were coming to visit her all the way from Oslo. She hadn't seen them for several months, and was busy preparing their favourite meal of *labskaus*.

After promising to look in again on their way home the girls took a short cut through a belt of trees and across the frozen lake, where a hole had been cut in the ice for the ducks and geese to drink.

Helma made a few purchases for her mother and then they went on to the Guide meeting, where they spent a happy morning making Christmas presents. In Norway gifts are exchanged on Christmas Eve, and every year

They were amazed to see a small girl out on the frozen lake

the Guides gave a party in their hall for the elderly people in the neighbourhood. Magda's father always brought them a fine tree from the forest, and everyone helped to decorate it. The Guides made gifts for every guest, and the old folk enjoyed singing the familiar carols.

The meeting over, the two girls set out on their journey home. The sun was hidden behind gathering snow-clouds as they left the village, and by the time they reached the far end of the lake the visibility was very poor; the mountains were hidden behind swirling grey clouds that seemed to fill the whole valley.

The Guides were just about to hurry on after a short pause to take off their skis, when they were startled to hear a child crying. Staring into the gloom, they were amazed to see a small figure in a red coat and fur bonnet standing out on the lake by the ice-hole.

Dropping their skis, they ran towards her, and had nearly reached her when a large dog bounded out from the surrounding trees, barking at the ducks that had come down to drink. He dashed up to the ice-hole, knocking the child off her feet. With a piercing scream, she fell backwards into the dark water.

Horrified, Helma and Magda raced forward. Magda still had her ski sticks on her wrists. Pulling them off, she flung herself down on the ice and thrust one of them down into the depths and swirled it round.

"Quick, hold my legs! I can feel something."

Helma grabbed Magda's ankles and hung on grimly whilst Magda plunged her arms into the freezing water. Her hands caught hold of something and she pulled with all her might.

A moment later she had the child in her grasp and pulled her out on to the ice. To their great relief, the little girl opened her eyes and began to cough and splutter and then to cry.

Helma took off her own anorak and wrapped the frightened child up in it and carried her as fast as she could through the trees to Frue Olsen's house. Magda, who was shivering with cold, fetched the skis and hurried after her.

Snow was beginning to fall, and as they drew near they heard someone calling, "Elsa, Elsa, where are you?" It was Frue Olsen's daughter, looking desperately worried. She had thought Elsa was making a snowman outside the door, but when she went to fetch her in for lunch there was no sign of her. She searched the little garden and sheds, thinking Elsa might be hiding for fun, and then began looking and calling for her along the various paths and tracks round the house. Her mother fetched old Thor the woodcutter, and he joined in the search, but they didn't dream a three-year-old would go as far as the lake.

"Quick, hold my legs!" cried Magda. "I can feel something"

Within minutes Elsa was in a wooden tub of hot water and then bundled up in shawls and tucked into a warm bed. Thanks to the Guides' prompt action she was none the worse for her adventure. After a glass of hot milk she soon fell asleep.

Elsa's mother overwhelmed the girls with thanks for saving her child's life. Frue Olsen explained that she had often told Elsa folk-stories about the *Noken* or water sprites who were said to live in the drinking holes in the ice in winter. Elsa must have wandered off down through the trees, and finding herself by the lake gone over to the ice-hole to see if she could see one! Luckily, she suddenly realised she was alone, and cried out, her frightened cries being heard by the Guides.

Outside, the snow-laden wind howled down from the mountains. Old Thor went off to tell the girls' parents they were safe and would return home in the morning.

Magda sat by a blazing log fire clad in some of her hostess's rather voluminous garments whilst her own were drying, and Helma set the table ready for the *labskaus* that was still waiting in the pot!

It was not long before the whole village heard about the rescue, and Christmas Eve that year was a specially happy one. Everyone wished each other *Glaedige Jul* as they gathered for the party, and there seemed to be more presents than ever round the brightly lit tree. Two of these bore Helma and Magda's names, and inside each was a gay knitted hat, scarf, and mittens, and an invitation to visit Oslo in the spring. The card was signed, *With love from Elsa and the Noken.*

13

Haggis Hunt in Scotland

by Joyce Burns
Illustrated by Sheila Graber

While English Guides were camping
In Scotland, wild and bleak,
They were given strict instructions
How their suppers they must seek.

While camping o'er the Border
They must taste some local fare,
So each Patrol were told how it
Could best a Haggis snare.

The Guides stalked in the forest
And searched and searched around.
They knew the Haggis would not be
A-nesting on the ground.

They looked into the branches
Of the pine-trees tall and straight,
And when the Thing was spotted
This was then its fate.

The hunters made a circle,
Just as instructions said.
Each closed one eye and hopped along
With a hand upon her head.

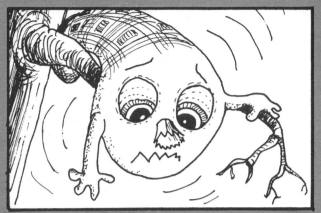

This sight so strange thus hypnotised
    The creature in the tree
That it became quite easy prey
    And was soon no longer free.

The Haggis was approached with care
    And in a net was lured.
The Guides were very gleeful
    As their suppers were assured.

The hunters stood in single file
    And did a smart turn right.
With pomp and pride they marched back home,
    Damp wellies gleaming bright.

Their booty was then handed to
    The cooks and dear QM,
Who were standing peeling turnips,
    And expressed their thanks to them.

At seven-thirty sharp that night
    (Camp meals are never late!)
The Haggis was piped to the feast,
    Held high upon a plate.

The Scottish dish was served to all
    And up went quite a cheer.
"Hurrah for neaps* and Haggis;
    We'll come again next year!"
                            *Turnip

15

Countryside Quiz

by Michael Edwards

1. What is the flat part of a bird's feather called?
2. Are acorns harmful to cattle?
3. What is caviar?
4. Which of these trees is associated with Christmas: yew, cedar or spruce?
5. Upon what does the grass snake chiefly feed?
6. Complete this country saying: "Clear moon —— ——."
7. Name two common garden birds that often choose odd nest sites.
8. What is a Camberwell Beauty?
9. Gaggle is the collective noun for a flock of what?
10. The Romans introduced the pheasant to Britain—true or false?
11. A male fallow deer is called a buck. What is the female called?
12. Where is Britain's only breeding pair of snowy owls?
13. To what family of birds does the redwing belong?
14. What is the white of an egg called?
15. How many species of snake are there in Britain?
16. We say a "flock" of sheep, a "pride" of lions. What term should properly be applied to a company of larks?
17. A lump sucker is (a) a leech, (b) a plant, (c) a fish?
18. We get pork from pigs. What do we get from deer?
19. Which owl often nests in farm buildings?
20. What is an ornithologist?
21. It has a green back, a red crown, and it hammers on trees. What is it?
22. Complete this saying: "As bald as a - - - -."
23. To what family of fish does the grayling belong?
24. Which two members of the crow family live in colonies?
25. What animal has a "frog" in its foot?
26. Complete this country rhyme: "Red sky at morning, ——— ———."
27. Which is England's largest county?
28. Which little freshwater fish builds a nest?
29. Wood hedgehog, sickener, and parasol are varieties of what?
30. What are lakes called in Scotland?
31. What is the series of enclosures in one of the colour pictures opposite and what is its use?
32. The bird shown in the picture attacking an intruder on its nest site lives only in the north of Scotland. What is the bird?
33. What is the name of the picturesque little bridge spanning the stream in the colour picture opposite? There are a number of them in this country.
34. The eggs in one of the black-and-white photographs belong to our largest wading-bird. Can you name the bird?
35. In some parts of the country farmers put wooden collars round the necks of sheep, as in the photograph. Why?
36. The fourth black-and-white photograph illustrating this quiz was taken with the light coming from behind the ferns. What is this type of picture called?

The Birthday Party

A NOISE Story for the Camp-Fire
by Delphine Evans

Make appropriate noises, such as those suggested in brackets

It was Carol's (*While shepherds watched . . .*) birthday, and she was waiting for the postman's knock (*knock, knock* or *rat, tat*). She could hear him whistling (*all whistle*) as he walked up the street. She looked out of the window and saw him open the gate, then heard letters fall on to the hall floor (*plonk, plonk*).

Mrs Bray (*bray*), who is Carol's (*Hark, the herald angels sing . . .*) mother, helped her open the envelopes and read the birthday greetings (*"Happy birthday to you"*).

Carol (*Christians awake!*) was having a party later, and Mrs Bray (*bray*) said she could help blow up (*blows*) some balloons. Carol (*O come, all ye faithful*) blew hard (*blows*), but found it took a lot of puff (*puffs*). She sat down to rest—right on top of a balloon, which her mother had just blown up, and popped it (*pop, pop*).

"I think I'll go and play with my dog (*barks*)," she said. "He wants a run."

She called the dog (*calls of 'Rover', 'Fido', etc.*) and went out of the door, which the wind banged to (*bang, bang*).

At last it was time for the party, and soon guests were knocking on the door (*knock, knock*). Carol (*Good King Wenceslas*) opened it and welcomed everyone.

First they played some games that made them laugh (*laughs all round*). Then Mrs Bray (*brays*) said it was time for tea, and there was a rush to the table. "Oh, I'm starving!" said someone (*gasps and other sounds indicative of a starving girl*). Everyone began to eat (*munching noises*) and to drink (*drinking noises*).

Before leaving the guests sang "Happy birthday!" (*all sing it*). **Make up your own noise story.**

Before the Storm

by Clare Thomas

A Guide of the 28th Company (Bryanston), Johannesburg, South Africa

Steamy ground waits,
  silence reigns.

Birds rustle their feathers uneasily,
Dogs shuffle and shift—
  but still
    silence reigns.

Flowers lift expectant faces,
Trees hold out branches to catch the first drops,
Stones await their return to the soil—
  the storm is coming.

Cigarette smoke settles in a cloud form,
Creased dresses crush past,
Tempers begin to brew,
  while milk starts to curdle,
    as the storm draws near.

Skipping dies down,
  balls bounce slowly,
Chatter eases,
  clouds gather,
    lower,
      glower.

Tenseness reigns
        and
          the
            storm
              breaks.

Stitch Puzzle

by Ruth Hoult

Can you find the different stitches by solving the clues?

Across
1. A support for a flower
4. It has links
7. A warm covering
8. Bad-tempered
9. You can get out of breath doing this

Down
2. A yachting term will help you to find these temporary stitches
3. A dog likes it, but a stitch needs *6 Down* with it
5. An insect
6. A fish with *3 Down*

Catch Crossword

A Challenge to Guides

This CATCH CROSSWORD was published in the *Sixer Annual for Cub Scouts*, and the Editor received irate letters from Cub Scouts and their Leaders complaining that they couldn't understand it and couldn't do it. Well, Guides, can *you* beat the Cub Scouts and solve the puzzle, which is presented here substantially as in the *Sixer Annual*?

Solve the clues just as you would an ordinary crossword —but don't be surprised at the answers; it's a *catch* crossword!

Across
1. Lines of people
2. To employ something
3. Guides should keep them open
4. At rest
5. Used by golfers, drunk by Guides
Down
1. When your Guider speaks you must be this
2. You must be this in a library
3. If you are the opposite, you are noisy
4. This is how your Guider likes the Company sometimes
5. This is what Guides playing games seldom are

1	2	3	4	5
2				
3				
4				
5				

Which Badges?

by Doris Nicholson

Which twelve Interest badges are referred to in the four paragraphs below?

1. "Isn't it odd," said Jane, "that Mary and I both have Interest badges showing a hand, while Sue has two hands on hers?"

"Yes," Mary agreed, "but I couldn't tell your friends where to go, and Sue's friends probably wouldn't understand me, either."

2. Anne and Sarah both wear a lion badge. Elizabeth has a snake on hers. None of them is particularly interested in wild life, though Sarah would like to go abroad and Elizabeth hopes to be a doctor one day.

3. There are three bird badges in Tonya's Patrol. Jill is not very interested in Carol's domestic birds, but Tonya need not study birds at all!

4. Mandy's hammer and Polly's sickle have nothing to do with Russia. Diana and Mandy use different kinds of paintbrush indoors, but Polly prefers to work outside.

Make a Patrol Flag

You're proud of your Patrol, so show the flag! It will identify you as the Swallows or the Kingfishers or the Robins or the Daffodils or whatever your Patrol is when you are in camp and on other occasions.

Here are some ideas for designs. Think up your own to fit your Patrol name. Your flag could include your emblem, if you wish, but elaborate on it in an original way.

For the Woodpeckers' flag, cloth and a plastic that suggests tree bark would be appropriate

Green shamrocks against a black background would look effective on the Shamrock Patrol's flag. A leprechaun figure on the staff and a green fringe would complete a striking design

The Peewits' flag could be finished off with a leather edging
Attach to the staff with a very neat lashing

Thistle Patrol, how about picking out your thistle design in this different way against a background of green and mauve?

The brilliant colours of the kingfisher could be blended to make a striking flag of cobalt-blue, chestnut, white and red for the Kingfishers

20

The Hills an' the Sea

The hills an' the sea,
An' the world an' me,
An' the hush o' lonely places;
The clean white road
An' the hay new-mowed
An' the men wi' sunburnt faces;
The cool of a hedge
On a mountain edge,
Where a wee stream wildly races;
An' them as will
Can have their fill
O' the roar and sob
O' the noisy mob
That crowds in the city places.

—St. John G. Ervine

Pioneering Puzzle

by J. Dening-Smitherman

How much do you know about pioneering? Find out by starting at square one, and working your way round the spiral. The last letter of each answer is the first letter of the next.

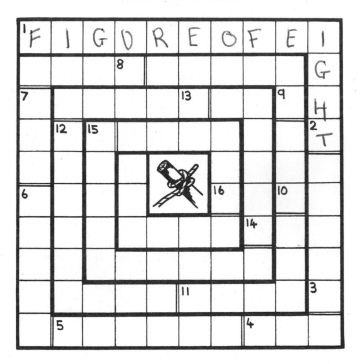

1. With this lashing you can join three spars (6-2-5)
2. This hitch is useful for moving logs, trunks etc. (6)
3. Most common and useful of knots (4)
4. Whipping rope-ends prevents this (7)
5. A knot with *no* uses! (6)
6. In rope-making, fibres are spun into this (4)
7. A man-made fibre, used extensively for ropes (5)
8. Wet ropes should be dried by these means (7)
9. Eye-splicing leaves the rope-end in this (4)
10. Ground-stakes in anchorages (7)
11. Type of rope made when four strands are twisted together (6-4)
12. Type of sheetbend used for joining ropes of very unequal thickness (6)
13. Nylon rope has this quality, an advantage for climbers (7)
14. Parbuckling is a method of moving this shape of objects up an incline (11)
15. The marline-spike hitch is used for these, which are made of rope (7)
16. Used for increasing the strain on a rope, this windlass has a foreign name (7)

Supersonic Guide

by Heather Armstrong

A Guide of the 1st Renhold Company, Bedfordshire

What will Guiding be like
In three thousand and one?

Space rocket badges
Maybe will be won.

Camping on planets
Venus and Mars;

Doing Eight-Point Challenges—
The points of the stars!

Studying flowers
That let off a vapour;

Eating pill-sweets
Wrapped up in paper.

Of course these things will happen
When you and I've died,
But I'd rather *not* be a
Supersonic Guide.

Countryside Creatures

Can you identify them? Where would you look for the originals? Are they to be seen in your area? Can you name the homes of the animals?

A young Guide at her first camp with the 1st Tunbridge Wells Company puts a shine on the tea dixie

Colour slide by Miss Daphne Pilcher

The Water Patrol of the 2nd Chesham Bois Guides' camp at Broadway

Colour slide by Miss E. Dollemore

Rough on the feet but lovely for a paddle, is the verdict of Guides of the Quantock District in camp at Crackington Haven

Colour slide by Mrs P. A. Briggs

Summer Snapshots

Good-Turn Eggs

The 25th Southport Company's unusual good turn is making eggs for patients at a local hospital. The Guides pierce the eggs with a needle, blow them over a bowl and wash and dry the shells

Chocolate is melted and poured into the shells and left to set. Then the shells are decorated. The finished eggs, ready for presentation, look too nice to eat

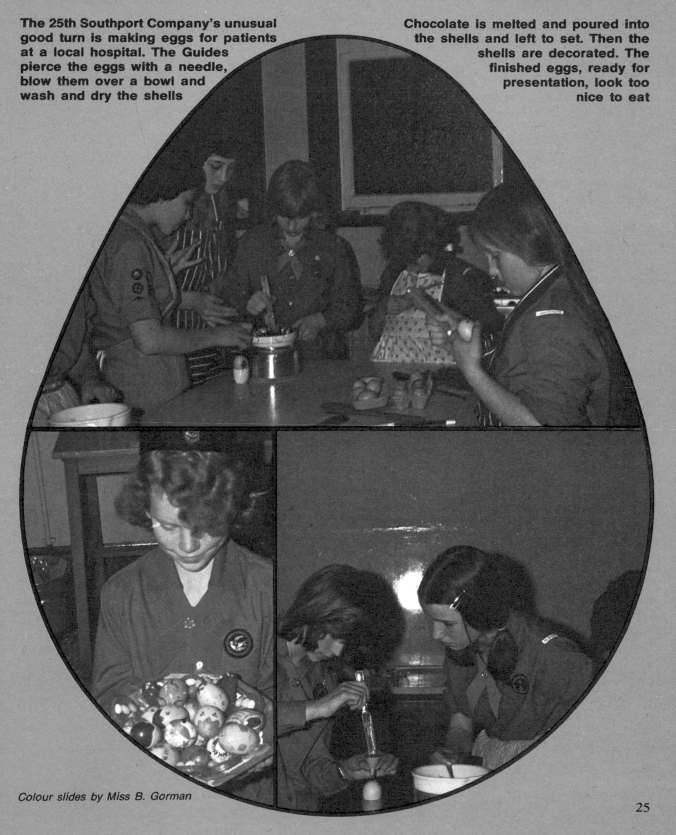

Colour slides by Miss B. Gorman

Cooking With a Difference

by L. Baker

These *dumplings "with a difference"* will turn your stew into a nourishing meal

Ingredients required

1. Eggs—two large ones to about a pound (450 grams) of plain flour
2. Flour, plain—amount depending on the number being cooked for
3. Lard or dripping
4. A little water

To about one pound (450 grams) of plain flour add two large eggs and about two ounces (56 grams) of melted fat and a little salt. Mix all into a thick doughy paste. A little water may be needed.

Cook directly in the stew, but if you are cooking for a lot it may be more convenient to cook in a pan of water brought to the boil and kept simmering.

Taking a teaspoon of this stiff mixture at a time, pop into the simmering water. You will find that it slips off the spoon easily in water. Do this until pan is full and simmer for ten to fifteen minutes.

Drain off water and add to stew for a few minutes, cooking to take on flavour of soup. Serve a generous portion to each person.

As this dumpling has eggs and fat in it, it is nourishing and filling, and also extremely tasty.

If you wish, add herbs at the mixing stage to give additional flavour.

This surely is a "dish with a difference!"

For *a camp meal "with a difference"* buy packet soups of the boil-for-five-minutes variety. The number of packets will depend on the number of people you are cooking for.

Buy also packets of proto-veg, the textured soya protein food. This is light, easily carried, and even when the packet is opened keeps indefinitely. Proto-veg can be bought at most health-food shops; it is very reasonably priced, goes a long way in use, is very filling, and has the protein equivalent of meat. It can be bought in three flavours: pork, beef, and natural. Small quantities or larger packs are available in two textures, mince and chunky.

The mince takes three minutes to cook, the chunky

about twenty-five minutes.

Following the directions on the packet, mix the soups with water. When this is done, add the proto-veg and simmer for the required time. As the proto-veg takes on the soup flavour you have a tasty, economical, very filling meal in next to no time. The washing-up required is minimal, as everything is cooked together.

Here's how to provide *potatoes "with a difference"*. Begin boiling your potatoes in the usual way, adding salt to taste. Now add curry powder to the water. The amount you add will depend on the quantity of potatoes you are cooking. Don't add too much at first. When the potatoes are nearly cooked, taste them and add more curry powder if necessary and cook a few minutes. Drain and serve in the usual way.

Finally, for another tasty, filling *dish "with a difference"*, try paprika potatoes. Ingre-dients required are onion to chop and fry, fat to fry onion in, salt for seasoning potatoes, and powdered paprika, which can be bought at most supermarkets.

Melt fat in the pan you are to cook potatoes in. Chop onion finely. About one large onion to 5 lbs (2¼ kilograms) of potatoes is the right proportion. Fry the onion in fat. Peel potatoes and cut into smallish pieces.

When the onion is lightly browned, take pan off heat and add paprika and salt. Use about three or four teaspoons of paprika to 2¼ kilograms of potatoes, but put in less rather than more, as you can always add more a few minutes before cooking is complete.

Add cut potatoes to the onion, etc. and just cover with water. Bring to boil and simmer till soft. Try for flavour and add more paprika if not tasty enough. The liquid you are left with can be served with the potatoes, which should be pinky-red and "mushy". Slices of bread can be "dunked" in this liquid, which is very tasty.

To make your meal more nourishing, chunky proto-veg, previously described, could be partially cooked in a separate pan and added at the last ten minutes of cooking to acquire the flavour of the potatoes. Fried sausages could also be cut up and added to this dish.

Rice "with a difference" can be made by adding a little curry powder to the cooking water.

Rice can also be cooked in a weak solution of packet soup; it absorbs the taste of soup completely, so don't add salt—or very little—when cooking in this way.

Try adding an Oxo cube to the water you are cooking rice or potatoes in. Again, watch the salt, as Oxo is itself salty. The number of Oxo cubes required will depend on the number of people you are cooking for. Add too little rather than too much, as more can always be added if required.

Now prepare *a cold meal "with a difference"*.

Ingredients required

1. **Long French-type bread—a couple of thick slices per person.**
2. **Eggs—about one to one and a half per person**
3. **Butter or soft margarine**
4. **A little salad-cream and salt to taste**
5. **Alternative to salad-cream: a little onion**
6. **Foil for wrapping bread in**
7. **Mixing-bowl.**

Hard-boil eggs—just. Cut loaf in half across the middle (not lengthwise). Scoop out most of the bread (do not throw away). Peel eggs and chop finely. Mix into a kind of stiff paste. Add butter to achieve this effect, and a little salad-cream to get a spicy taste. Salt to taste. If preferred, instead of salad-cream add grated onion (raw); this tastes very nice in chopped eggs.

With a knife, spread a little butter inside the hollow loaf and then pack in the egg-mixture, placing two halves of loaf, facing each other, to form a whole loaf again. First dampen the outside of loaf, then wrap in foil and heat through in a hot oven.

Serve your savoury egg-roll in thick slices with vegetables or alone after a soup.

The bread you scooped out of the loaf can be rolled and squashed into small balls, then dropped into each dish and the soup poured over them.

Assault Course

One false step and they'll be in!

Patrol Work

by the 5th Reigate Company

Patrol planning

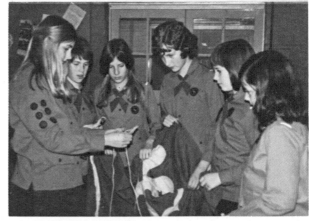

Learning colours

Colour prints by Miss B. Wing

No, they're not practising for the Olympics. They're the 10th Bromley Guides trying out the assault course at Buckmore Park Scout Activity Course, Kent

Colour slides by R. and A. Squires

Puzzle Words

by H. J. Askins

Clues Across
1. Most of these are the down answers

Clues Down
2. Coach, bus or railway
3. Direction finder
4. Line of points at the same height
5. Red triangle especially for young people
6. Framework of lines for reference
7. MS

Clues Across
1. These are the down answers

Clues Down
2. and 4. Colourful and kingly but could be a very angry ruler of an empire
3. Yellow but not made of sulphur
4. See 2 DOWN
5. Brown with pale rings but no curly hair
6. Large, cabbage, wood and green-veined but not very colourful

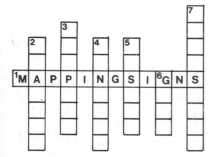

Ha, ha, ha

GUIDE: I'm sorry, conductor; my dog has eaten my ticket.
CONDUCTOR: Then you'll have to buy him a second helping, won't you?

P.L.: What picture do you like best on your TV, Rosie?
ROSIE: I think the one of my brother.

A mother sardine and her small offspring were swimming in the sea when a submarine passed by.
"Don't be afraid," the mother comforted the youngsters. "It's only a can of people."

MUM: Can you describe the girl who scratched your face, Sally?
SALLY: I'd rather not—that's what I was doing when she went for me.

Pig Crossword

Clues Across
1—River animal (5)
4—Fox's hole (5)
7—This man went to mow (3)
8—Male duck (5)
9—Box for horses (5)
10—Area of cabbages (5)
12—It slides off a duck's back (5)
14—Female sheep (3)
15—Direction sign (5)
16—Eagle's nest (5)

Clues Down
1—Not even (3)
2—Farm vehicle (7)
3—Species of deer (3)
4—Snake-like fish (3)
5—Early riser (7)
6—Gardening instrument (3)

10—Could be used to shoot (3)
11—To cut in pieces (3)
12—Very small (3)
13—Cereal (3)

Make a Compass

Harold Ridgway Shows You How

To make this simple working compass you will need a thin postcard, a small piece of thicker cardboard, a pair of compasses, a setsquare, a safety-razor blade, a fine needle about 3.8 cm ($\frac{1}{2}''$) in length, a craft knife, a magnet, an eraser, and some adhesive.

First prepare the compass-card (Fig. 1) by drawing two concentric circles on the postcard. The larger circle measures 5.7cm ($2\frac{1}{4}''$) in diameter, the smaller one 2.5 cm ($1''$). By means of a setsquare mark out the points, as shown in the diagram. Place a 1p coin over the inner circle and hold it in position. Cut round the with a craft knife. Remove the inner circle.

Continue by preparing the two cross strips (Figs. 1A and 1C). These are cut from the remainder of the postcard. Each one measures 7.9cm ($3\frac{1}{8}''$) in length and 1.3cm ($\frac{1}{2}''$) in width. Take one of the strips, and at the centre on the underside make a small round depression with a rounded-point tool. Do not pierce the card.

Now form this strip into the bridge (Fig. 1B). The top of the bridge measures 2.2cm ($\frac{7}{8}''$) in length; the two sides are 1.0cm ($\frac{3}{8}''$) in length, and the end flaps each 1.9cm ($\frac{3}{4}''$). Mark these measurements on the strip, score them with a knife, and bend into shape.

The strip, Fig. 1C, has a hole .5cm ($\frac{3}{16}''$) in diameter, punched through the centre. Next, take the razor-blade and, for safety, mask the edges with narrow tape. Magnetise the blade by stroking it one way only with a magnet. Then glue the blade to the underside of the strip, as shown in Fig. 1D.

Attach the two strips to the underside of the compass-card. First glue the bridge in position and, underneath this, the magnetised strip. The latter strip is secured parallel to the lines marking north and south on the face of the compass-card.

Now press the needle into the centre of the eraser. The compass-card is then placed upon the needle. The head of the needle should be seated in the small depression in the centre of the bridge. It should always be in this position when the compass is in use. Fig. 2 shows all the parts of the compass in the correct order: **A** is the compass-card, **B** is the bridge, **C** is the magnetised strip, **D** is the needle and **E** the eraser. For the sake of clarity in the diagram, the bridge and the magnetised strip are shown before being glued to the compass-card.

The compass-box is formed from cardboard, which is 17cm ($6\frac{3}{4}''$) square (Fig. 3). The bottom of the box is 7cm ($2\frac{3}{4}''$) square. The sides are 5cm ($2''$) in width. Score the dotted lines and cut the solid lines. Discard the corner areas shaded by lines, leaving flaps 1.3cm ($\frac{1}{2}''$) in width, for glueing to the inside of the box.

The box-lid is made in the same way. Add twice the thickness of the cardboard to the measurements given. Glue the corner flaps to the outside of the lid. All that now remains is to attach the eraser with glue to the bottom of the box.

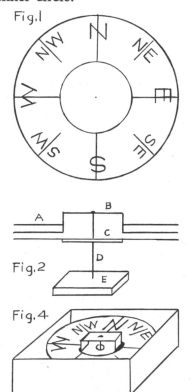

Fig.1

Fig.2

Fig.4

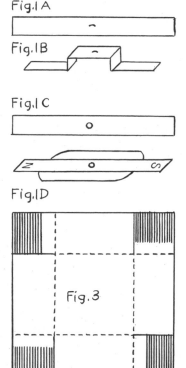

Fig.1A

Fig.1B

Fig.1C

Fig.1D

Fig.3

Friends

Friend to Deaf People badge

A member of the 10th Bromley Company teaches the finger alphabet to other Guides working for the Friend to Deaf People badge

The owl is not at all averse to the petting bestowed on it by 10th Bromley Guides on a visit to a Kent bird sanctuary

Colour slides by R. and A. Squires

Overseas Campfire

A small part of the worldwide Guiding family in Singapore: United Kingdom Brownie and Guide, Singapore Guide, and New Zealand Guide, with a Commissioner

Guides and Brownies of Australia, New Zealand and the United Kingdom join with Singapore members of the far-flung Guiding family in a campfire singsong in Singapore

Photos by Sgt. Muddeman

The Silver Belt

by Merril Brown

One moment Jackie was sitting in the drowsy classroom, the next minute she was walking along the silver road. Looking back on it afterwards, she could not determine the precise moment at which the change was effected. She was sitting in the classroom with the hot sun streaming through the all-glass, left-hand wall. A tired fly was buzzing intermittently against the window-pane; the girls' heads were nodding, and the voice of Mr Carter, the senior history master, floated over Jackie's head like a haze of smoke over the rooftops.

Jackie yawned and fingered her Guide badge. She was thinking of the Guide meeting that evening and half listening to the history lesson. Mr Carter was expounding on the world-shaking changes of the industrial revolution. He was warming up to his favourite topic.

"It was a time," he insisted, "of great change, of revolution in more than industry. There was a dawning in men's minds of the wonders of things to come, of the possibilities of scientific invention. If we could speak with a person from the period, miraculously transport him to the present day and ask him what

he felt and thought, we might have an inkling of the change that was taking place in men's minds, as well as in industry."

Jackie could not be sure, but it was somewhere at this point that she was no longer in her desk but on the long shining ribbon of a road. There was no point at which the classroom vanished or became less clear. She did not remember rising from her seat. She was walking along the silver ribbon and the sun was as hot as it had been through the classroom windows.

She went on walking without any thought as to where the road led. She had no feeling of weariness. Her head felt rather light, her step was light too. The road, she remembered, did not seem to be of any tangible, recognisable substance, but it was firm to the tread.

Suddenly, the road sloped down, and Jackie was certain she must be dreaming because it seemed to lead into the roof of a

large building, which had not been visible until now. There seemed to be other buildings on either side, but the road sloped so quickly and steeply that Jackie's feet nearly slipped from under her. She felt as if she was propelled downwards. She experienced the sensation which one meets in a dream—of waking suddenly with a jerk just as one is about to fall heavily.

There was a voice saying, "Stand back! She will be shaken at first."

Then followed a murmur of voices. Then the first voice spoke again.

"It is common for a subject to faint after the first shock of transportation through Time. Remember the case of the subject from the Roman period. Do not question the subject until she is fully conscious. She is already waking. Note the typical dress of the twentieth century of the late Christian epoch."

"Excuse me, Professor," put

in a higher-pitched voice. "Is the subject of the First Atomic Age?"

"Of the First Atomic Age, but before the Great Atomic War," answered the first voice. "Man had not yet fully realised the potentialities of the power he had harnessed. It needed the example of the Great Atomic War, called in that period the Third World War, to make him fully aware of the extent of his discoveries. This was, you remember, an age of great change. The first satellites had been launched. They had landed a man on the moon. Man stood on the threshold of a new era of discovery."

Jackie reflected that the owner of the voice sounded like a female edition of old Carter holding forth to 5A on a similar topic. Half-consciously, she remembered that she should have been in 5A classroom, undergoing the rigours of a double period of history—modern, eighteenth to twentieth centuries.

Wearily she opened one eye, and closed it again quickly. Her brief glimpse had been of a group of figures in a semi-circle around her, all eyes in her direction. She thought of pinching herself to find out if this was a dream or not. Before her bemused mind could induce her hand to move, however, she felt a touch on the shoulder.

"Open your eyes," said the voice. "You are quite safe."

"That's what you think," thought Jackie, but she opened both eyes. She sat up. They were still there.

"Have no fear," said the voice, which belonged to a tall, lean woman at her side. "You will come to no harm."

Jackie realised she was sitting on a chair. At least, it wasn't exactly a chair—more a seat on long, spindly legs. It was very comfortable.

"We hope you will be able to help us," went on the tall lady professor. "We are studying the late Christian period and have taken the liberty of bringing you here to give us some information."

Jackie could think of no reply.

"I was telling the boys and girls," continued the Professor,

"Have no fear," said the voice. "You will come to no harm"

"that a subject from the period would, no doubt, regard the era as one of great change. They persuaded me that it was necessary to produce proof of this. We have done this before. Last month we had a very interesting subject from the early Christian epoch."

Jackie managed to find her voice. "But why choose me?"

"The girls wanted someone of their own sex and age." The Professor smiled. "We had a pompous Roman senator last week. He wasn't much help."

"I don't suppose I shall be much help, either," ventured Jackie.

"It is always interesting to meet anyone from the past," was the reply.

Jackie caught a glance from one of the girls. She looked at the group. They regarded her curiously. "In much the same way," thought Jackie, "as 5A regard old Carter's film-strips." She realised that her dream had taken her into a school of the future. Obviously she had been reading too much science-fiction lately. It was like something out of a TV series: spirited into the future by a time-machine gadget which was standard use for school history lessons. It was too fantastic.

Yet here she was sitting in the spindly chair next to a machine with a complicated mass of switches and buttons and surrounded by a crowd of boys and girls dressed in tunics which looked something like Roman togas, except that they were made of some silvery substance she had never seen before.

Suddenly Jackie felt extremely hot and uncomfortable in her own school uniform.

"Will you answer some questions?" asked one of the girls.

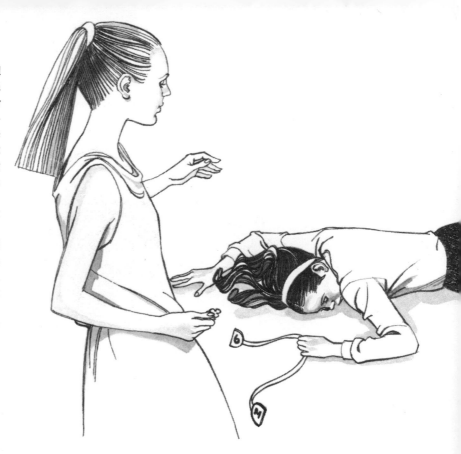

She caught at the belt of the tall girl as she fell

"Yes, all right," Jackie grudgingly agreed.

"What year is this in your time?"

"Nineteen seventy-nine."

"Which country do you live in?" was the next question. The girl pronounced the word country as if it was a strange word she would not normally use.

"England."

"That is one of the islands on the outskirts of the European block," put in the Professor. A loud bleeping noise interrupted her. "I must leave you for a while. Continue the questions." She disappeared silently.

The girls and boys stared at Jackie.

"Not a very interesting specimen," sneered one boy.

"Specimen yourself," retorted Jackie. She felt hot, tired and annoyed at the whole proceedings.

"What's this?" asked a tall girl, pulling Jackie's Guide badge from her lapel and examining it.

"My Guide badge," answered Jackie.

"What's that?" asked the girl. "I have heard the word Guide. Is it a Movement?"

"What do you do?" questioned a fair-haired girl next to her.

"We belong to a Company and work in Patrols. We have hikes and camps and we learn a lot of useful things and make a lot of friends," said Jackie.

"I have read about this Movement," the first girl remembered. She fingered Jackie's badge. "This will be an interesting memento."

"Hey!" cried a boy. "You know we should not touch the subjects we transport. Put it back, M6."

"Yes, give it back to me," said

forbidden. All stand back. We'll just hope we can get her back to her own century before there are any ill effects. This is another lesson wasted."

Jackie tried to open her eyes. The Professor was bent in concentration over the controls of the machine. Jackie was fighting to stay awake, to say something, but her head was still swimming. She sat up with a conscious effort and opened her eyes. A bell was ringing. Old Carter was saying ". . . to be handed in by break tomorrow."

Chairs scraped back as the class prepared to go to lunch.

She had never seen the belt before—or had she?

Jackie got to her feet slowly.

"Don't forget Guides tonight —it's the campfire meeting," called her chum, Biddy. "See you then. Where's your badge? You were wearing it when you came in."

Jackie put up her hand and felt her lapel. The Guide badge had gone. Surely it could not have been taken by the girl from the future? No, that was too fantastic! She collected her books and started towards the door.

"Hey, Jackie, you've dropped something," Emma Evans called to her as she passed.

Jackie stooped and picked up the object she had dropped. She stared at it. It was a belt, made of a thin silvery substance she had never seen before—or had she?

Jackie, and made a grab for the badge.

The girl stepped swiftly back. Jackie, quite angry now, jumped from her seat to seize the girl, but caught her foot in one of the spindly legs of the seat and fell. As she did so, she caught at the belt of the tall girl who had taken her badge. The belt came away in her hand. She lay on the floor for a few seconds, feeling rather dazed. She could hear a babble of voices.

"Get her into the chair."

"The Professor will be furious. You know what happened when that Stone Age boy . . ."

"Give her a drink."

Jackie's head was raised, and someone put a cup to her lips. She drank and tasted something light and bubbly. She felt dizzy and her head spun. Far away she heard the Professor's voice.

". . . told you before you must not touch the subject, and to give her something to drink is quite

The Village Church

**Written and Photographed
by George H. Haines**

The porch at Berringto
Shropshire

The parish-church is a promising place in which to "discover the past", as recommended by the *Guide Handbook*. It is often the oldest building in a village, older than the cottages, the farms, the trees and the hedges. The features of the church will sometimes tell the story of the village.

THE TOWER: Most churches have a tower or spire, which may act as a landmark. Some churches had a beacon to guide travellers at night. In districts where attack was likely the tower was built specially strong so that it could be used as a refuge.

THE MASS DIAL: In pre-reformation days masses were held in churches at set times during the day. To indicate the times of the masses simple sundials were scratched on the wall and a hole made to hold a stick to cast the shadow. These are usually near the priest's door. Often at some later time figures for the hours were added.

Mass dial at Wixford, Warwickshire

THE PORCH: The porch was an opportunity to provide an impressive entrance to "God's house". In the past the porch was used for many different purposes. Business was transacted there, and some porches still have the little desk at which contracts were signed. The coroner's court sometimes sat on the seats in the porch. Important announcements and proclamations were put on the church door so that everyone would see them. Some porches have an upper room where the mass priest slept. When invasion was feared this was used for storing ammunition. Look for the stoup, which held holy water used to make the sign of the cross on entering.

The font at Woolstaston, Shropshire, where an earlier font is used as a base for a later one

THE FONT: The font is often the first object you notice inside a church. In early times adults were christened by standing in the font, which was low and tub-shaped. Later it became the custom to christen children, and then the font was raised on a pedestal. Look at old fonts for

The lord of the manor's pew at Stokesay, Shropshire

the marks of staples used to lock the lid to prevent "witches" stealing the holy water.

PEWS: At one time there were no seats in churches except for stone benches along the wall. When sermons became longer, seating was built. In some old churches there are box-pews with a door from the aisle. The lord of the manor often had an impressive pew with tall sides and a roof.

PULPIT: Pulpits were built higher to enable the preacher to speak easily to those in the gallery. Imposing three-decker pulpits may still be seen in some churches. The clerk used the lowest level; the next was used during the service; and the preacher delivered his sermon from the topmost stage.

THE LECTERN: The lectern is the rest on which the Bible is placed for the reading of the lesson. Some are simple ledges, but others are in some quite elaborate shape; a favourite is the eagle, symbolising the Gospel being carried all over the world.

For Your Hallowe'en

October 31st is the night when witches are abroad, riding on their broomsticks, with black cats, hooting owls, cobwebs and spiders about. A smoky cauldron filled with a magic brew, and other Hallowe'en trappings, will help to evoke the right "spooky" atmosphere for your party.

If you hold the party out of doors you could make a camp-fire and boil soup for the witch's brew. Everyone could bring her own mug, plate, etc., and perhaps contribute food or drink—to be shared out.

Dress up as witches, wearing blankets and black head-dresses (made out of handkerchieves). Witches' hats could be made out of black cardboard.

Think up games to play beforehand, songs to sing, rhymes to guess, ghostly stories to tell, etc.

Hallowe'en Invitation Card

For an indoor party keep your decorations for table and room in orange, green, yellow and black. Make novelties—e.g., orange-coloured or green baskets—and fill them with sweets, one for each guest. A centrepiece could be the witch round the cauldron or a large jack-o'-lantern.

Hang jack-o'-lanterns on all lights in the room. String or wires with witches on broomsticks flying around, and black cats, moons, etc. suspended across the room or from the ceiling, would show in an exciting way that it's Hallow-e'en.

Send invitations to your friends in the form of a jack-o'-lantern cut out in folded cardboard and coloured orange. Inside write something like this:—

How to Make a Witch

1. Twist a pipe-cleaner around a small piece of twig for the legs, and twist into shape
2. Twist another pipe-cleaner round for the body and let the two open ends at the top hold the paper-ball head (see 4) in position. Secure this with sticky tape
3. Add another pipe-cleaner for the arms and twist the hands on to the twig
4. Make a small ball of crêpe paper (orange) for the head. Add a long nose with bits of crêpe paper. Mark in other features with a ball-point pen or paints
5. Tie some bits of raffia or strips of paper on to the end of the twig for the broom
6. Dress the witch with scraps of black material, or use paper and paint it afterwards. Make a handkerchief head-dress and tie on firmly with black cotton. Don't bother to sew the witch's clothes; just tie on with black cotton

Photo: Hemel Hempstead Echo and Post

How now, you secret, black, and midnight hags! What is't you do?—*Macbeth, Act IV, Scene 1*

Come to our hallowe'en party
And taste the witch's brew—
Whoooooooooooooooooo!
We'll be expecting youoooooooooo!
The place is . . . . . . The time is . . . . . The
day is . . . . . . .Whoooooooooooooooooooo!

Party

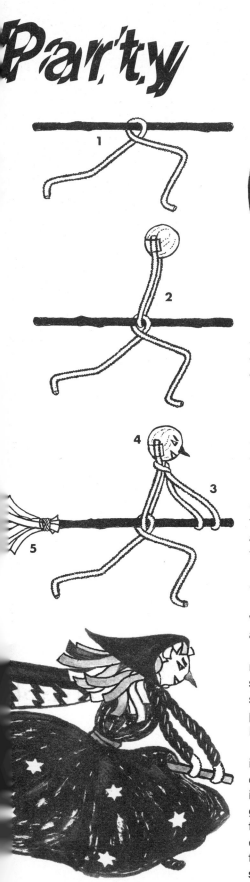

The Witch's Cauldron

Three twigs tied together Cauldron made with black cardboard

Flames a square of orange crêpe paper

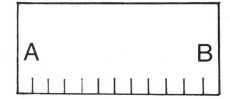

A										B

Make 1.3cm (½″) cuts along one side

Fold over A-B. Stick with gum. Fold over cuts

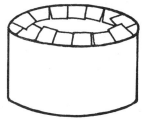

Cut out a small circle. Stick over the cuts to make the base

Cut out a strip of cardboard for the witch to stir the cauldron with

How to Make a Jack-o'-Lantern

Blow up a balloon to the size you require. Tie up the mouth with string. Cover the balloon with strips of newspapers dipped into paste. The whole balloon must be completely covered with four or five layers of paper. Don't cover the mouth of the balloon.

Leave for 24 hours to dry out. Let the air out of the balloon by untying the string, and pull out the balloon, which can be used again if you are careful not to tear it.

When dry, paint orange colour.

Cut out the top opening; add wire to each side for a handle and twist round.

Cut out two eyes and a large mouth. Build up the nose with scraps of paper pasted on (this should be done before you paint the face) or cut out a small hole for the nose.

Hang the lantern on the light in the room, or place in a window with an electric torch inside. The lantern looks really gay when the light is shining through. It could be used as a centrepiece for a table decoration and filled with fruits, sweets, etc., if desired.

Pet Economies

This gerbil likes to play hide-and-seek in a teacup

Photograph by Alan Band Associates

L. BAKER Suggests Means of Cutting the Cost of Keeping a Pet

Our pets are hamsters and gerbils. Their bedding has to be changed often, and this can be expensive. It costs us nothing! We simply recycle out-of-date telephone directories, which make excellent clean, soft, warm bedding. But don't rush off and destroy this year's!

Not all paper is suitable for use in this way, as the print wipes off too easily; but the G.P.O. directories and yellow pages have excellent print and are quite safe to use. We detach several pages at a time and scissor them into narrow strips. The strips can be stored in a plastic bag till required. A similar type of shredded-paper bedding can be bought at most pet-shops, but why buy? If your family doesn't have a telephone, ask a friend to save her old copies for you.

A gerbil is quite happy to do his own recycling. He is a perfect disposable unit for those cartons used for the weekly shopping and that take up precious room in the dustbin. Instead of popping them in the bin, we push them one at a time into our gerbil's cage and watch him go to work on them. Papier-mâché egg-boxes (not the polystyrene type), cat and dog-food cartons, and practically any clean carton excepting soap-powder ones will keep him happy. This means that less sawdust—only a very thin sprinkling—is needed, as he shreds a carton so finely that it soon forms part of his floor litter for digging in.

Another economy to practise is not to buy pre-packed food. It is much cheaper, and just as good for your pet, if you buy the ingredients loose by the pound and mix them yourself.

The main ingredients of food for hamsters and gerbils, etc., is sunflower seeds. These are sold loose as parrot-food at about twenty pence a pound; all the other ingredients are about eight pence a pound; these are mixed corn, flaked maize, rolled oats, wild birdseed, rabbit pellets, etc. So a pound of parrot-food and about a quarter of a pound of all the others will last your pet far longer than an expensive little packet of pre-packed food.

Grow Your Own Seeds

If you have a free patch of soil you could grow your own sunflower seeds. Sunflowers flourish like weeds even in poor soil. About April just pop several sunflower seeds into the soil. About September, after the flower has died off, open the flower-head and you will find that each flower-head contains nearly a pound of choice seeds for your pet.

If at any time you have melon, don't throw away the seeds from the middle. Hamsters and gerbils love these, either as they are or washed and dried and added to their seeds. Any left-over bread too can be baked slowly in the oven to harden and then given to your pets to nibble. Broken biscuits and odds-and-ends of cereal can likewise be added to their food.

When Mother is preparing vegetables or stew for the family ask her to save you the tops and bottoms of the carrots. Pop these in water and put in the fridge, where they will keep fresh and juicy all the week for your pet.

You will be able to think up other economies for yourself, but be careful not to endanger your pet's well-being in any way by giving it wrong food. If in any doubt, ask a knowledgeable adult or consult a book on your particular pet.

Things to Make

Faith Blanchard Shows You a Neat and Effective Way to Display Your Christmas Cards

You require stiff paper or thin card of any colour, plain or patterned. You must be able to cut through two thicknesses together. You will need scissors, brass push-through paper-fasteners, and drawing-pins.

Take a strip of paper or card 8cm wide. Score a line down the centre longways. On one half of the strip rule a pencil line 1cm in from the edge, and another line 1cm in from the scored central line. Rule lines at 1cm intervals across this half strip. Fold the strip in half lengthwise.

Omitting 2cm at the top and bottom, cut diagonal slits through two thicknesses on both edges, using your pencilled squares as a guide. Overlap the uncut ends when fastening strips together with a paper-clip, and make two or three long strips to be hung up by drawing-pins.

Whatever the shape of your Christmas card you should be able to insert it with two upstanding points at the bottom to hold it up and one central flap at the top to hold it back.

Cards will not be damaged if wanted after Christmas, and the strips can be rotated at the paper-clip junctions and stored in a pile in a small space.

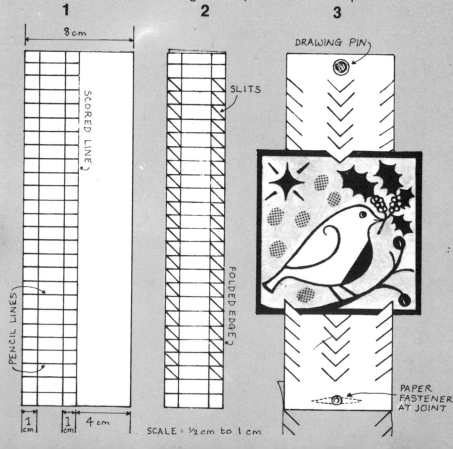

Doctor Livingstone

by
Gary Keane and Neville Randall

1823. AGED 10. A JOB IN THE MILL. STUDYING LATIN AS HE WORKED. SAVING ENOUGH TO ENROLL AT 23 AT ANDERSON COLLEGE, GLASGOW. TO READ MEDICINE AND DIVINITY.

1840. A MEETING WITH ROBERT MOFFAT, ON LEAVE FROM HIS MISSION STATION IN BECHUANALAND.

"WILL I DO FOR AFRICA?"

DECEMBER 8. AS A MEMBER OF THE LONDON MISSIONARY SOCIETY, HE SAILED FOR THE CAPE.

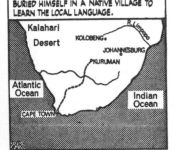

1841. KURUMAN. 500 MILES FROM CAPE TOWN. LIVINGSTONE JOINED THE MOST NORTHERLY MISSION IN SOUTH AFRICA. BURIED HIMSELF IN A NATIVE VILLAGE TO LEARN THE LOCAL LANGUAGE.

Kalahari Desert
KOLOBENG
R. Limpopo
JOHANNESBURG
PKURUMAN
Atlantic Ocean
Indian Ocean
CAPE TOWN

1843. HE MOVED NORTH ON HIS OWN. TO FOUND A NEW MISSION AT MABOTSA NEAR THE LIMPOPO. A LION CRUNCHED HIS SHOULDER. AND DAMAGED HIS LEFT ARM FOR LIFE.

1845. MARRIAGE. TO MARY MOFFAT. NORTH AGAIN. TO ESTABLISH NEW STATIONS AT CHONUANE, AND KOLOBENG ON THE EDGE OF THE KALAHARI DESERT.
RUMOURS REACHED HIM OF A VAST DESERT LAKE, NEVER SEEN BY WHITE MAN. WITH INHABITANTS TO BE CONVERTED TO CHRIST.

1849. JUNE 1. KOLOBENG. LIVINGSTONE SET OFF ACROSS THE KALAHARI DESERT, WITH A HUNTER, COTTON OSWELL. *TWO MONTHS LATER* THEY DISCOVERED LAKE NGAMI. THE ROYAL GEOGRAPHICAL SOCIETY AWARDED HIM £25. BRITAIN HAILED AN EXPLORER.

1851. NGAMI WAS TOO UNHEALTHY FOR A MISSION. NATIVES SPOKE OF A LAND OF MIGHTY RIVERS TO THE NORTH. HE SET OFF TO FIND IT. REACHED A DEEP FLOWING RIVER, 500 YARDS WIDE. THE ZAMBESI.

ANOTHER PARTY PASSED HIM. ARAB TRADERS DRIVING CAPTIVE AFRICANS TO THE COAST TO SELL AS SLAVES.

A NEW MISSION WAS BORN. TO STOP THE SLAVE TRADE BY FINDING A ROUTE TO OPEN UP AFRICA TO COMMERCE AND CHRISTIANITY.

1852. THE MAP OF CENTRAL AFRICA WAS A BLANK. LIVINGSTONE RESOLVED TO DISCOVER AND OPEN IT TO THE WORLD. SENT HIS WIFE AND PROTESTING CHILDREN BACK TO SCOTLAND.

"THE MARK OF CAIN IS ON YOUR FOREHEAD. YOUR FATHER IS A MISSIONARY."

JUNE 8. HE SET OUT FROM THE CAPE WITH A CARAVAN OF OX-WAGONS FOR THE ZAMBESI. ON A JOURNEY TO LAST FOUR YEARS. REACHED LINYANTI, CHIEF TOWN OF THE MAKOLOLO TRIBE. WELCOMED BY THEIR CHIEF.

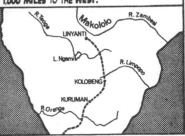

1853. NOV. 11. OFF AGAIN, UP RIVER. BY OX-WAGON AND CANOES. WITH 27 ZAMBESI PORTERS, AND ALMOST NO STORES. *OBJECTIVE:* TO FIND A NEW ROUTE THROUGH UNKNOWN LANDS TO THE COAST. 1,000 MILES TO THE WEST.

R. Teoge
Makololo
R. Zambesi
LINYANTI
L. Ngami
R. Limpopo
KOLOBENG
KURUMAN
R. Orange

 Published by arrangement with the Daily Mail, London

1853. NOV.-DEC. OFF UP THE ZAMBESI. PADDLING. WALKING. RIDING OX-BACK. DODGING ALLIGATORS AND HIPPOPOTAMI. BARTERING MILK AND MEAL FROM VILLAGES WHO HAD NEVER SEEN A WHITE MAN BEFORE.

1854. MARCH. OUT OF MAKOLOLO COUNTRY. BEYOND THE ZAMBESI. TRUDGING OVERLAND. WET. FEVERISH. HUNGRY. MENACED BY HOSTILE TRIBES DEMANDING TRIBUTE FOR PERMISSION TO PASS. IN CONSTANT FEAR OF ATTACK.

THE PORTERS COULD STAND NO MORE. THREATENED TO GO HOME.

"I WILL GO ON ALONE."

"WE WILL NEVER LEAVE YOU. WHEREVER YOU LEAD, WE WILL FOLLOW."

MORE ON MONDAY.

1854. APRIL. INTO PORTUGUESE WEST AFRICA. 300 MILES TO GO. TRUDGING ON FOOT. TORMENTED BY MOSQUITOES. UNABLE TO SLEEP. WEAK WITH DYSENTERY.

TOO DELIRIOUS WITH MALARIA TO KNOW THE DAYS OF THE WEEK OR THE NAMES OF HIS MEN.

MAY 12. FIRST GLIMPSE OF THE SEA. THE PORTERS GAZED IN AWE. MAY 31. HE STAGGERED INTO LOANDA, REDUCED TO A WALKING SKELETON. AFTER A THOUSAND MILES IN SEVEN MONTHS.

THE NAVY OFFERED TO TAKE HIM HOME. LIVINGSTONE REFUSED.

"I HAVE GIVEN MY WORD TO MY FOLLOWERS TO BRING THEM BACK. I NEVER BREAK A PROMISE."

HE PREPARED FOR ANOTHER 1,000-MILE TREK. BACK TO CENTRAL AFRICA.

1854. SEPTEMBER 20. LOANDA, WEST AFRICAN COAST. LIVINGSTONE SET OFF. RESTORED TO HEALTH. RE-EQUIPPED WITH MUSKETS, AMMUNITION, CLOTH AND BEADS. FOR THE 1,000-MILE TREK BACK.

INCESSANT RAIN. MORE MALARIA. CRIPPLING ATTACKS OF RHEUMATIC FEVER. A BUFFALO CHARGED HIM. A HIPPOPOTAMUS UPENDED HIS CANOE.

1855. SEPT. 10. HE RETURNED, WITH HIS FOLLOWERS TO LINYANTI.

THE TRADE ROUTE TO THE WEST WAS IMPRACTICAL. HE RESOLVED TO FIND A NEW ONE. DOWN THE ZAMBESI TO THE INDIAN OCEAN. ANOTHER 1,000 MILES TO THE EAST.

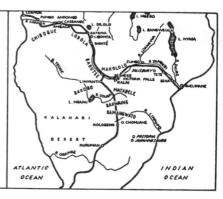

1855. LINYANTI, CENTRAL AFRICA. LIVINGSTONE SET OFF BY CANOE. WITH A NEW MAKOLOLO TEAM. TO FOLLOW THE ZAMBESI DOWNSTREAM TO THE INDIAN OCEAN. 1,000 MILES TO THE EAST.

NOV. 16. FIVE MILES AHEAD, FIVE WHITE COLUMNS ROSE UP TO THE CLOUDS. HIS FOLLOWERS CALLED THEM "THE SMOKE THAT THUNDERS."

HE PADDLED ON. LANDED ON A MID-STREAM ISLAND. PEERED DOWN A CRACK. THE MILE-WIDE RIVER CRASHED VERTICALLY TO MORE THAN 300 FT. BELOW. IT WAS THE LIP OF THE WORLD'S GREATEST WATERFALLS.

HE CALLED THEM VICTORIA.

1856. MAY 20. FOUR YEARS AFTER LEAVING CAPE TOWN. LIVINGSTONE REACHED QUELIMANE ON THE INDIAN OCEAN. FIRST EUROPEAN TO CROSS AFRICA FROM WEST TO EAST. THE MAP WAS REDRAWN.

DEC. 9. BACK TO BRITAIN. A HERO. WROTE "MISSIONARY TRAVELS". LECTURED TO UNIVERSITIES. RECEIVED IN AUDIENCE BY QUEEN VICTORIA AND THE PRINCE.

1857. DEC. 4. A LECTURE TO CAMBRIDGE UNDERGRADUATES.

"I GO BACK TO OPEN UP A PATH TO COMMERCE AND CHRISTIANITY. DO YOU CARRY ON THE WORK I HAVE BEGUN."

A NEW CRUSADE WAS LAUNCHED.

1858. MAR. 12. LIVINGSTONE SAILED FOR AFRICA. WITH FIVE BRITONS. AND A PADDLE STEAMER DESIGNED FOR THE ZAMBESI. SET UP BASE CAMP AT KONGONE, IN THE ZAMBESI DELTA.

AUG. 17. UP THE ZAMBESI BY STEAMER TO PIONEER A TRADE ROUTE TO CENTRAL AFRICA. REACHED THE KEBRABASA RAPIDS. NO WAY THROUGH. LIVINGSTONE TURNED BACK.

1859. UP THE ZAMBESI TRIBUTARY "SHIRE". STOPPED BY CATARACTS. FORWARD ON FOOT. TO A VAST LAKE, 350 MILES LONG. HE HAD DISCOVERED LAKE NYASA, RENAMED MALAWI TODAY.

MORE ON MONDAY.

1861. KONGONE. BISHOP C.F. MACKENZIE ARRIVED. WITH AN OXFORD AND CAMBRIDGE MISSION TO NYASALAND. TO SET UP A PERMANENT STATION. LIVINGSTONE TOOK THEM UP THE SHIRE. RETURNED TO KONGONE AND...

...31 JAN, 1862. MET HIS WIFE MARY AND THE BISHOP'S SISTER TO TAKE THEM TO THE MISSION. THE BISHOP SET OFF TO MEET THEM. CAUGHT FEVER ON THE WAY. AND DIED.

MARY DEVELOPED MALARIA. DIED IN APRIL. WAS BURIED UNDER A TREE. THE MISSION WITHDREW TO THE COAST. THE SLAVE TRADE CONTINUED. CENTRAL AFRICA STAYED CLOSED AND HEATHEN.

LIVINGSTONE RETURNED HOME ALONE. HIS EXPEDITION HAD FAILED.

1865. AUGUST. LIVINGSTONE LEFT BRITAIN FOR HIS LAST EXPEDITION. BOUND FOR THE MOUTH OF THE ROVUMA BETWEEN MODERN MOZAMBIQUE AND TANZANIA. TO EXPLORE NYASA AND FIND THE FABLED SOURCES OF THE NILE.

1866. HE SET OFF UP RIVER. WITH 13 INDIAN SEPOYS, 10 MEN FROM THE JOHANNA ISLES, NINE FREED SLAVES TRAINED IN INDIA. AND A FEW AFRICAN BOYS. TREKKED ROUND THE SOUTHERN END OF LAKE NYASA.

SEPOYS, JOHANNA MEN AND FREED SLAVES DESERTED. TWO WAIYAU WENT OFF — WITH HIS MEDICINE BOX. HE PLODDED ON, WEAK WITH FEVER AND HUNGER. TO DISCOVER — IN 1867 — LAKE MOERO. IT EMPTIED INTO A RIVER HE HOPED WOULD BE THE NILE.

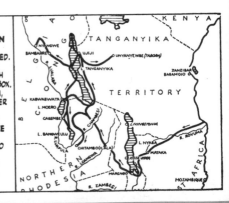

JULY, 1869. THREE YEARS ON THE MARCH. WITHOUT MEDICINE TO COMBAT DYSENTERY AND MALARIA. ACROSS LAKE TANGANYIKA, 400 MILES LONG. TO UJIJI TO FIND STORES EXPECTED FROM ZANZIBAR. THEY WERE LOST OR STOLEN.

OVER THE LAKE AGAIN. A LONG TREK TO THE LUALABA — FLOWING NOT INTO THE NILE BUT THE CONGO. SICKENED BY SLAVE TRADERS' SLAUGHTER. SLOWLY BACK, WEAK AND ILL, TO THE LAKE AND UJIJI AGAIN.

FOUR DAYS LATER, DESTITUTE IN CENTRAL AFRICA. HIS SERVANT, SUSI, RAN TOWARDS HIM WITH EXCITED SHOUTS.

"AN ENGLISHMAN! I SEE HIM!"

1871. NOV. 10. UJIJI, TANGANYIKA. A WHITE TRAVELLER APPROACHED, WITH A CARAVAN FLYING THE AMERICAN FLAG. SUSI RAN TOWARDS HIM.

"I AM SUSI, THE SERVANT OF DOCTOR LIVINGSTONE."

"IS DOCTOR LIVINGSTONE HERE?"

THE STRANGER WALKED THROUGH AN EXCITED AFRICAN CROWD. TOOK OFF HIS HAT.

"DOCTOR LIVINGSTONE, I PRESUME?"

HE WAS HENRY MORTON STANLEY, SENT BY THE NEW YORK HERALD TO FIND LIVINGSTONE, ALIVE OR DEAD.

THEY EXPLORED THE LAKE TOGETHER, TO SEE IF IT EMPTIED INTO THE NILE. AT THE NORTHERN END THEY FOUND A RIVER, FLOWING IN.

STANLEY RETURNED TO REPORT HIS SCOOP. LIVINGSTONE CONTINUED THE SEARCH.

1872-3. LIVINGSTONE STAGGERED ON. STILL SEEKING THE NILE. STILL GETTING WEAKER. DYING FROM DYSENTERY. HIS FOLLOWERS CARRIED HIM IN A LITTER TO THE VILLAGE OF CHITAMBO.

1873. APRIL 27. THEY BUILT A HUT OF BRANCHES, REEDS AND GRASS. HELPED HIM STUMBLE INSIDE. HE WROTE HIS LAST NOTEBOOK ENTRY: "KNOCKED UP QUITE".

MAY 1. 4 A.M. CHUMAN AND SUSI ENTERED THE HUT. LIVINGSTONE WAS KNEELING BY HIS BED AS THOUGH IN PRAYER. HIS CHEEKS WERE COLD. "GREAT MASTER" WAS DEAD.

1873. HIS FOLLOWERS DRIED HIS BODY IN THE SUN. WRAPPED IT IN CALICO, BOUND IT IN BARK. AND CARRIED IT, WITH HIS INSTRUMENTS AND PAPERS, 1,500 MILES TO THE COAST.

1874. HIS COFFIN, STILL GUARDED BY ONE OF HIS AFRICAN BOYS, WAS BROUGHT TO BRITAIN. TAKEN TO WESTMINSTER ABBEY. AND BURIED IN THE CENTRE OF THE NAVE.

HIS RELICS RETURNED TO BLANTYRE. TO THE TENEMENT HOUSE WHERE HE WAS BORN TO FORM A MEMORIAL — VISITED BY MORE THAN TWO MILLION — TO THE MAN WHO OPENED AN UNKNOWN CONTINENT TO THE WORLD.

The Countryside

by Caroline Hudson

A Guide of the 4th Bromsgrove Company

Swiftly the fishes swim in the sea,
Swiftly the swallows fly from a tree,
Slowly the ladybird crawls on a leaf,
While slowly the beetle creeps underneath.

Swiftly the rabbit hops into his burrow,
Swiftly the tractor is making a furrow,
Slowly the tortoise creeps along;
The fox steals a chick, and he's in the wrong.

Swiftly the fox by the hunt is followed,
Swiftly on horseback the bugle is bellowed;
Slowly with cheese in his mouth the mouse
Creeps along to his tiny house.

Hike Tools

Make these useful tools for hiking and camping. You need strong wire. Cheap coathangers will do excellently. Beg Daddy's wire-cutters and pincers or pliers and set to work to make **A** for dampers; **B**, a toasting fork; **C**, a pothook for hanging your small dixie or billycan over the fire; **D** for toasting your cheese-dreams—this needs a wooden handle bound on, which gives you a chance to use your whipping knowledge; **E**, a griller (cut a square piece of tin and hammer it flat. Then with the pliers bend a rim down each edge and hammer it flat over the prongs of your fork. Bind on a wooden handle, as for the cheese-dream toaster).

"Her mother said she wasn't to miss her daily piano practice"

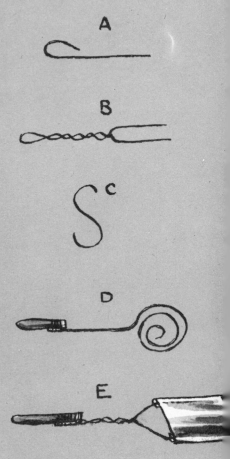

48

Mousey Masterpieces

"Exploring the arts" in a different way, Rita Greer has produced a gallery of old masters with heads of mice, dogs or cats in place of the original faces.

This original, self-taught artist has given an amusing "new look" to the masterpieces of Rembrandt, Vermeer, Hilliard,

Velasquez, and others.

Now, Guides, put on your thinking-caps and see if you can devise an interesting new art form—not necessarily with paints, but perhaps with natural materials, as with the twigs illustrated on pages 8-10.

Colour slides: Alan T. Band Associates

1. Is it Nelson, Napoleon, or Popeye the Sailor?

2. An original Rembrandt and its mouse-head version

3. Would Rembrandt's Captain of the Guard be amused by his latest portrait?

4. The Duke of Wellington changes from a Goya to a Greer

Ceremonies With a Difference

The World Badge

Guide Companies and Brownie Packs think up interesting and unusual ways of celebrating Thinking Day and of presenting Promise ceremonies.

A Manchester Company lit candles on Thinking Day and arranged them in the shape of an arrow, which was pointed to the World Flag.

An East London Company tied a greeting card to a balloon released by each Guide in the hope that a Guide in another country would find it. In fact, several cards reached people as far away as France.

Hampshire Guide Companies held a song contest based on the theme of Britain in Europe and received a variety of interesting songs, the winning one of which was composed by the 6th Chandler's Ford Company.

An unusual Promise ceremony was carried out by one Guide Company. The whole Company climbed to a hilltop, each Guide with a torch. When the Promise badge was pinned on a new Guide, all the torch beams were focussed on it, and the Guides sang "Whene'er you make a Promise".

Guide Law Game

by Jean Howard

Here's a game that will help you to remember the ten Guide Laws.

The Company stand in a circle. One Guide outside holds a baton or ruler or other object. She runs round outside the circle, finally stopping behind one of the Guides. She taps on her shoulder a number of times representing one of the ten Laws and asks, "What Law will you give me?"

The Guide must reply, "A Guide is friendly and a sister to all Guides," if tapped four times, or "A Guide is obedient" if tapped six times, and so on.

The Guide questioned must answer before the Guider conducting the game counts ten. If she answers correctly, she takes the baton and proceeds round the circle. If she answers incorrectly, the other Guides tell her the correct Law, and the first Guide continues round the circle.

This game could be followed up by a discussion about the Laws and how these can be observed more fully in daily life.

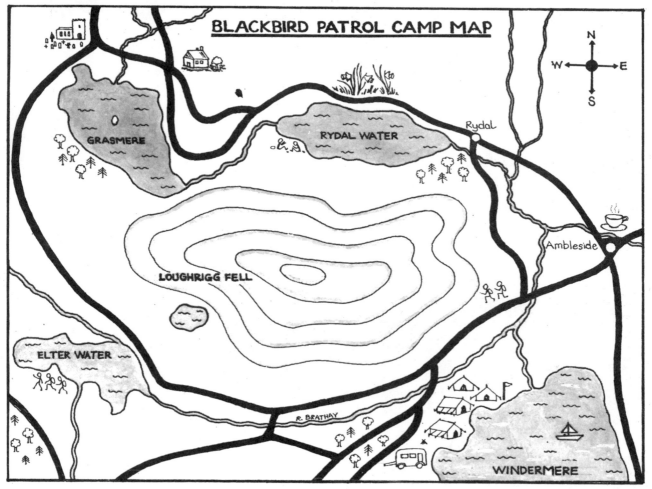

Make a Camp Map

Suggests Dorothy Ryan

Why not make a map of your camp this year? If you draw it on a large piece of poster paper it will make a lovely pictorial record for the wall of your Patrol corner. If you keep a Patrol logbook in which you enter outstanding events, you could translate these into pictures on your map. Each member of the Patrol could contribute.

At camp, make notes and draw a rough map of the camp-site and its surroundings and add symbols to represent activities and events. Then you can make your large-size map when you get home, colour it, and fill in places of interest visited, adding little pictures where appropriate, and perhaps snapshots.

The sketch on this page of a camp-site in the Lake District will illustrate the idea, though on a small black-and-white map it is not possible to show much detail. Can you see the tents we camped in, the lanes we hiked along, the boat we had on Windermere, the tea we enjoyed at Ambleside, Wordsworth's cottage, the churchyard and daffodils at Grasmere, and the fells we climbed?

Your map will be much better than this, and it will be in colour. It will enable you to live those delightful camp days all over again—for a long time.

Campers and Hikers

On a hike nearer home, Guides of the 7th Tonbridge Company take a well-earned rest
Colour print by Miss J. Homewood

Will she fall in?

Far from their High Wycombe home, these Guides of the 7th (Union Baptist) Company hike in Switzerland from their second home at "Our Chalet"
Colour print by Miss C. M. Church

After the feast the wash-up
Colour prints of 1st West Preston Guides by Miss D. Stromwell

Eagle Guides

Emergency Helper is one of the badges needed for the Eagle badge

Nine Chililabombwe Guides gained the top Guide badge of Zambia, the Eagle badge, which was presented to them at the Jubilee camp at Lusaka celebrating fifty years of Guiding in Zambia

In a lovely floral setting these Guides enjoy working for the Flower Arranger badge, one of the several badges to be gained for the Eagle badge award

Two of the Guides working for the Artist badge

Colour slides by Mrs K. M. Hobongwana

# of Zambia

Sweet Smells and Spices

POT POURRI
by M. G. Pearson

In the days before aerosol air-fresheners were invented, many people used a pot pourri to keep their homes sweet-smelling. The name means literally "rotten pot"—quite the wrong name to give to this fragrant blend of dried flowers and spices.

The nice thing about a pot pourri is that there is no fixed recipe; you use whatever flowers you have available, or choose the ones you like most. Any strong-scented ones will do. Lavender is perfect, because it keeps its perfume when dried. So too are roses, japonica-apples and bayleaves: the choice is up to you.

Pick the flowers when they are full out but not beginning to drop, on a warm, dry day. Pick the petals off the flower-heads and spread them out on an old tray. Leave them in a warm place (an airing cupboard, for example) until they have dried out completely.

Mix the petals together in a bowl. Now add your herbs and spices; again, the choice is up to you: nutmeg, cinnamon, cloves, perhaps a little lemon-peel and almond essence. Blend them gradually, a little at a time, until you are satisfied.

Now take a jar with a tight-fitting stopper and put a layer of your mixture in the bottom, about 1cm thick. Sprinkle on top a thin layer of salt, then add more mixture, then more salt, in alternate layers until the jar is filled up.

Put the stopper on and leave the mixture to mature for several weeks. It should be ready for use by the autumn. Just unscrew the stopper and the perfume of your pot pourri will fill the room. When it begins to fade, tip it out into a dish to make it last longer.

POMANDERS
by
Jacqueline M. Sylvester

The word pomander is an English corruption of the French pomme d'ambre (amber apple). Originally a pomander was simply an orange hollowed out and filled with spices or with a sponge soaked in aromatic vinegar. In the Elizabethan period it was replaced by a silver pomander, often enamelled and jewelled and more delicately perfumed. These pomanders were round perforated objects, only about one inch (2.5 cm) in diameter, and they opened either horizontally or in segments like an orange. They were extremely common amongst the "upper classes" and used by both men and women. Cheaper ones were made in hardwood with silver mountings. In an age when hygiene and sanitation were so bad they were something of a necessity. It was thought they warded off disease; nobles would sniff at them when going through the city, doctors or clergymen might use them when visiting pestilent areas. The pomander would be carried in a pocket, or worn at the waist or round the neck, for easy access. You have no doubt seen the pottery ones in the shops today, filled with sweet-smelling herbs and decorated with flowers or pretty scenes. However, it is quite a simple matter to make your own pomander similar to the ones first used centuries ago.

How To Make Your Own Pomander

All you need are an orange, cloves, and a ribbon about 1.3cm ($\frac{1}{2}$") in width. Tie the ribbon around the orange (which should preferably have a thin peel), so that it divides it into quarters. Then push the cloves into the orange, placing them close together and making sure all the exposed peel is covered. Wrap the orange in tissue-paper and leave to dry out in a warm place. The top shelf of the airing cupboard is an ideal spot. Drying-out takes about ten days to a fortnight; check on it from time to time and allow longer if necessary. When it is ready remove the ribbon, which will have become discoloured, and replace it with a fresh piece. If you wish, you can give the pomander a dusting of your favourite talcum powder. Do this by putting some talc and the pomander in a polythene bag and then gently shaking off the excess powder.

Simple Things to Make and Wear

by L. Baker

CAMP APRON

Make this serviceable and even pretty plastic apron for a few pence. You could take it to camp for when you do chores. It's light and easy to pack.

You need one plastic carrier-bag, either an ordinary plain one or one with a pretty design on the front; a length of tape or ribbon or even string; a pair of scissors.

Take two pieces of tape, ribbon or string, long enough to tie round your waist. Cut into two pieces and tie one piece to each of your carrier-bag handles.

Next, cut off the bottom of the carrier-bag so that it is straight across the bottom.

Now you have a disposable apron.

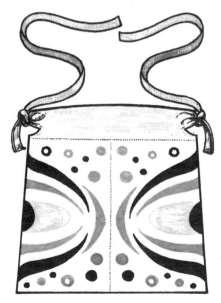

NYLON GRASS SKIRT

To make a twirly dancing skirt for yourself or for a younger sister, you require old nylon stockings and tights—the more the better; a sewing-needle; brown sewing-cotton; sharp scissors.

1 Select one pair of tights, preferably with a ladder-free body. Put these carefully on one side.
2 Cut all the legs from the remaining tights and put with any old stockings you may have.
3 Take the pair of tights that you put on one side and carefully cut open up the seam under the legs for 7.5cm (3″) or so. You can now step into the tights through the hole and pull up around the waist in the usual manner. Leave the legs hanging down on either side of you.
4 Taking one of the stocking legs you have cut off, tuck it under the edge of the body part so that it is more or less on a level with the legs you have left attached. Sew firmly in this position. As the tops of stockings are wider than the tops of tights you may find it necessary to pleat stocking tops together a bit before sewing in position. Proceeding in this manner, sew the legs next to each other till they go round the nylon body.
5 Decide on what length you want your skirt. Then carefully cut off the foot of each leg at an angle to form a point and give a pretty finish to the edge of the skirt.
6 You are now ready to wear your skirt or give it to a younger sister as a present. This skirt can be washed. If done in the shorter version, it makes a very attractive costume for an elf in a Brownie play or something of that kind. It twirls beautifully when its wearer dances.

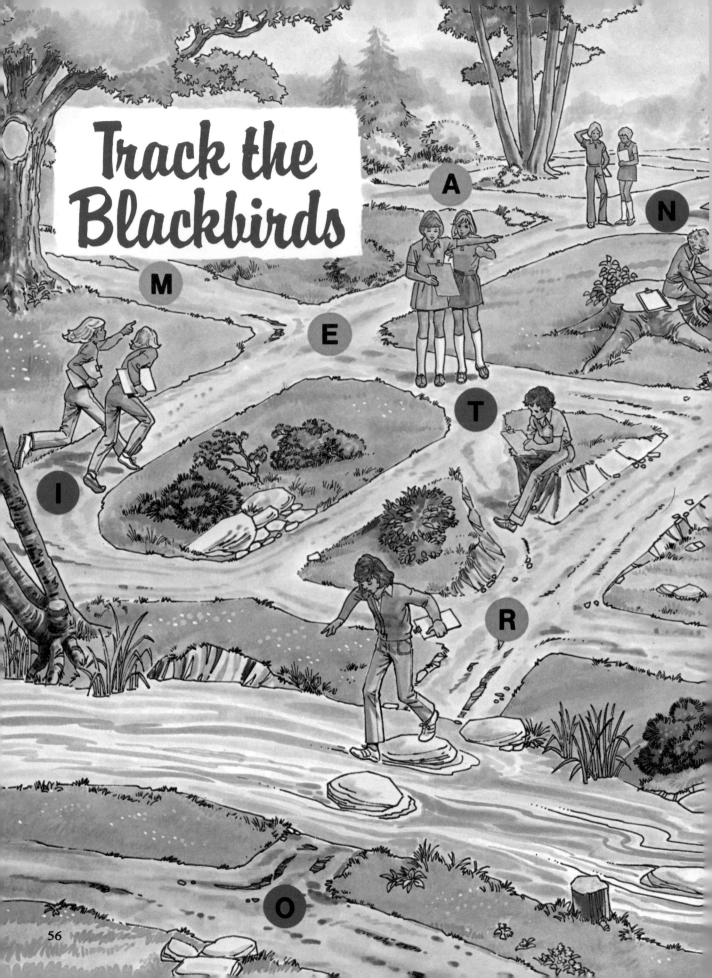

Track the Blackbirds

The Blackbird Patrol have laid a trail from camp and challenged the three other Patrols to follow it. They left compass directions and woodcraft signs for the trackers. Can *you* follow their trail? Here's a clue to guide you: the Blackbirds are very good at orienteering.

Going Down!

by Jean Howard

Shirley looked out of the window at the gathering storm clouds. The afternoon had been hot and oppressive, and she thought she had better take her mackintosh with her to Guides that evening. Her family had recently moved into a flat on the top floor of one of the new ten-storey blocks, and she still found it strange to see the tops of the trees instead of brick walls and pavements.

After tea, she changed and gathered up some things she needed for her Patrol to make some coloured felt animals for the District Bazaar. She put them into her case with some she had finished, and, taking her

mackintosh on her arm, said goodbye to her mother and crossed the landing to the lift. She pressed the button. While she was waiting for the lift to come up, she was startled by several flashes of lightning and a distant peal of thunder.

At the seventh floor she was joined by Elaine and Gillian, who were Guides in her Company, and by Mrs Parry and her little grand-daughter, Amanda. Mrs Parry didn't often leave the flat, but the child had been so fretful in the heat that she was taking her to a nearby shop for an ice-cream before bedtime.

When they were all inside, Shirley closed the doors, and the

lift moved off again.

"Next stop, ground floor," called Gillian, pretending she was in the big store in the High Street.

But there was a sudden jerk that threw them all backwards. The lights went out, and the lift came to a halt between the second and third floors.

Amanda let out a scream and clutched Elaine, who nearly lost her balance and stepped backwards on to Mrs Parry's toe.

For a moment Shirley was horrified at the thought of being stuck in the lift, but when she heard the others crying and calling out she realised she must keep calm. "A Guide has courage and is cheerful in all difficulties," she murmured, remembering the seventh Law.

Luckily she had slipped her torch into her mackintosh pocket, because the Guide hall was down a rather dark road. She groped about till she found it. She switched it on. Immediately all began to feel less alarmed, though Amanda continued to cry. Elaine produced a small roll of peppermints and gave her one. Then Shirley sat down on the floor, and, taking a penny from her purse, made it spin on the floor. The little girl found this very amusing, and her tears stopped.

Then Shirley asked Gillian to hold the torch. When a sudden clap of thunder crashed overhead, she suggested that they sang a song to cheer themselves up.

The Guides began to sing "If you're happy and you know it", as cheerfully as they could, but another even louder crash made Amanda jump and she started to scream again. Elaine tried to comfort her, but she became quite hysterical. Then Shirley thought of the felt animals in her case. Amanda forgot her fears at the sight of them, and began to play with them on the floor, whilst Gillian made exciting animal noises, and joined in the game.

Suddenly there came the sound of banging on the top of the lift. They all listened intently. With a coin Shirley tapped out a message in Morse code on the side of the lift: HELP. WE ARE STUCK. She didn't think it likely that her message would be understood, but to her delight a message was tapped back: POWER FAILURE. HOLD ON. SOON HAVE YOU OUT.

Shirley assured the others that help was at hand. About five minutes later the lights went on again, and they all blinked in the sudden brightness. Slowly the lift began to move downwards to the second floor. The doors opened, and they were free! Shirley carried Amanda out, and Elaine and Gillian gave Mrs Parry a hand.

A grinning engineer greeted the Guides. "Who's the signaller?" he asked. "You?" as Elaine pointed to Shirley. "I learned Morse in the Scouts years ago; never forgotten it. Comes in handy, don't it?"

"It helped us all to know that help was coming soon," agreed Shirley. "Thank you very much."

"Thank *you!*" said the engineer, and his thanks were echoed by Mrs Parry and Amanda.

"The felt animals look rather grubby now," Shirley remarked to the other Guides as they hurried out to get to the Guide meeting in time.

"They came in handy," said Gillian. "They kept Amanda happy, and we can easily make some more."

"Tell you what," said Elaine thoughtfully: "Knowing the Morse code is jolly useful. I've just made up my mind to go in for the Signaller badge."

With a coin, Shirley tapped out a message in Morse code

Becoming a Homemaker

Create Artistic Flower Holders
by Brenda Morton

The Homemaker Badge

LARGE CONTAINERS
Put flowers in small glass dishes. Arrange dishes in large container. Put moss over top or fill gaps with pebbles

LOG OF WOOD
Carve hole. Fill with heather for permanent rustic decoration. Put some modelling clay in hole if heather springs out

EGGSHELLS
Paint outside of shell if desired. Mix plaster-of-Paris. Pour this into a tinfoil cap. Before it is set, place eggshell in it. Eggshell will hold water and tiny flowers

WILDFLOWERS
Mould little vases from balls of plasticine. Press to make deep hollow for water. Flatten base. Leave no cracks or water will escape. Plasticine gives a soft "earthy" effect that enhances the simplicity of the wildflowers

NAPKIN RINGS
Put flowers in a tiny glass dish or plastic carton inside a napkin ring. The dish will not be seen. Silver rings are particularly effective

WALNUT SHELLS
Half a walnut shell makes a tiny novelty flower-container. Mould a pedestal base of plasticine to prevent the shell from rolling. Put tiny flowers in Florapak

What did they bring to the little Boy—
what shining thing, what priceless toy?

They had no jewels, priceless, old—
no cup of silver, no crown of gold.

But the dog looked down at the Child with love,
as if in its deep, soft-glowing eyes
it caught a glimpse of Paradise.

The ox's frown turned gentle, kind,
as he pondered in his slow oxen mind
what kind of thing was this tiny Stranger,
sleeping so gently in the manger.

And a bird on its passage through the town,
flew into the stable and looked around
to try, in its small, bird way to see
what was the source of this mystery.

They had no riches a hand could hold—
only their heart's clear-shining gold,
and they gave what they had, their love, to the
   Stranger,
the Babe that was sleeping in the manger.

Gifts

by Virginia Scott Miner

Reprinted by permission from the Christian Science Monitor

Mountain Crossword Puzzle

Clues Down
1. Opposite to stop
2. Tailless monkey
3. Vast expanse of water
4. Female
5. On a Brownie Six emblem
9. Camp near a fresh supply
10. Used in puddings
11. Part of the body
12. Grown-up boy
13. Your brother is your father's

Clues Across
3. Signal of distress
6. Jack Horner put his thumb in it
7. Often eaten in a sandwich
8. More than wonder
12. Go climbing up these
14. Tie it with rope
15. Not straight

Puzzle Page...Puzzle Page...Puzzle Page...Puzzle Page...Puzzle Page...

Puzzle Page...Puzzle Page...Puzzle Page...Puzzle Page...Puzzle Page...

Which Interest badge is Sarah working for? To find out, draw or trace the drawings in the frames on the left into the blank frames with the same numbers on the right, and you will know.

Badge JIGSAW

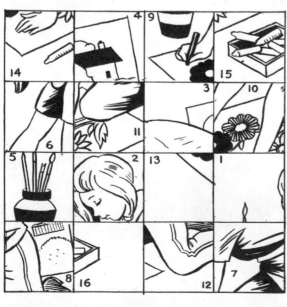

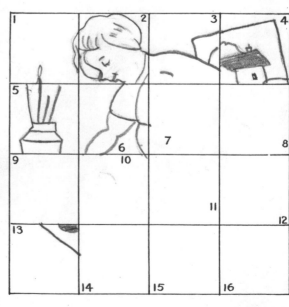

It's a Giggle

Mrs Gale's Mistake

by Nancy Bryant

The Girl Guides asked
Old Mrs Gale:
Please, something
For our Jumble Sale.
Said she, "I think,
Upon a nail,
In our old attic,
Mr Gale
Has hung a mirror
Old and pale.
I'll give that
For your Jumble Sale."

Her husband, Bill,
Let out a wail
When he heard of
The Girl Guides' sale.
He said, "That glass
Was Chippendale!"

After the sale,
They knew not where
The glass had gone.
Gale tore his hair.
For weeks he searched
In great despair;
But now they're both
A happy pair.
The mirror's back
Above the stair.
It turned up still
Without repair
At the Girl Guides'
Christmas Fair.

"I'm just going to vacuum my tent"

"One thing, there's no stairs to climb!"

Fancy dressers at the 1st Tunbridge Wells (St. Luke's) Company summer camp
Colour slide by Miss Daphne M. Pilcher

Fancy Dressers

Winners of the 2nd Shepperton Company's Hallowe'en fancy-dress competition include a witch and a terrifying headless horseman
Colour slide by Miss A. M. Stevens

'Pick the Pictures' Prize Competition

All you have to do is to put the six delightful pictures on the next page in the order in which you like them. For example, if you like **F** best you put **F** as number 1, the letter of your next choice as number 2, and so on down to number 6. Whatever your age you have as much chance as anyone else of winning the wonderful prize of a new bike for yourself and £50 for your Company.

The Editor has made his choice. If your first choice agrees with his, you will gain three points; if your second agrees with his, you will gain two points; for each of the others that agrees, one point will be awarded. The competitor with the most points will win the grand double prize. Something of equal value to the bike can be chosen, if preferred.

On the page overleaf is space for you to say in about a hundred words what you like best about the *Girl Guide Annual.* Take care with this write-up, because it will be taken into account if there are competitors with the same number of points.

Complete both sides of the entry form and post it to "PICK THE PICTURES" PRIZE COMPETITION, PURNELL BOOKS, BERKSHIRE HOUSE, QUEEN STREET, MAIDENHEAD, SL6 1NF, to arrive not later than March 31, 1979. The winner will be notified as soon as possible after this date.

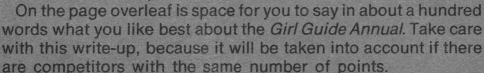

Just put the picture's letter in the order of your choice

1 ....
2 ....
3 ....
4 ....
5 ....
6 ....

THE GIRL GUIDE ANNUAL "PICK THE PICTURES" COMPETITION ENTRY FORM

My name is ....

My address is..

....

....**My age is**............

My Company is ....

....

My Guider's name and address is ....

....

....

....

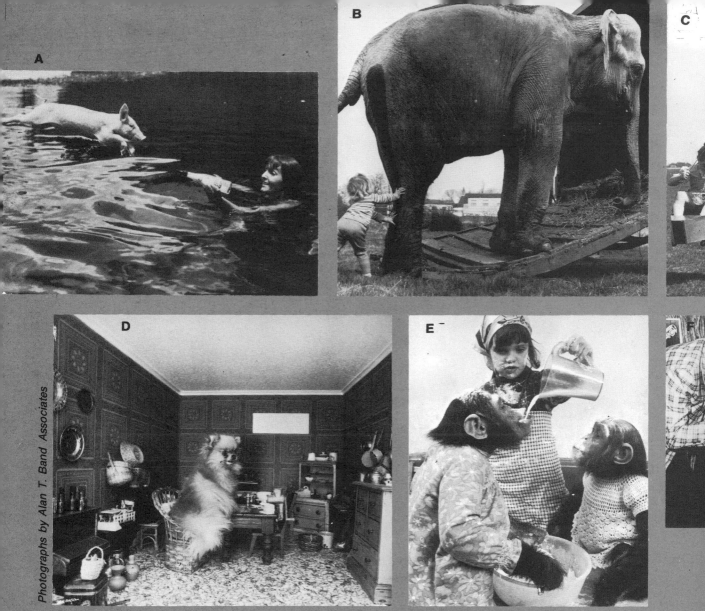

Photographs by Alan T. Band Associates

A. Pigs can't fly but this one can jump—even into water if there's a tempting bottle of milk waiting

B. The circus folk couldn't get the elephant into the van, so they called his friend, Kitty, who gave that extra push that persuaded four tons of elephant to move

What I like best about the *Girl Guide Annual*

CROAKER COLLEGE

C. What on earth is this? It's a human roundabout, Walter Cornelius, of Peterborough, who thinks nothing of swinging a couple of children round in swing-boats by man-power only

D. This Pomeranian dog lives a life of luxury in his own house, which is furnished in Victorian style and is, of course, centrally heated

E. Tracey Clews, of Southsea, enjoys cooking, and her pet chimpanzees love helping her to make pastry, especially when a stop is made for drinks

F. Would you believe that there's a college for frogs? Well, here are the pupils, being taught by Professor Steed, of California, U.S.A., to hop in tune with a record

Things to Make

Daphne Rockall Shows You How to Make an Oriental Neck Choker with Matching Bracelet and Belt

You will need silver foil or cellophane, pencil, ruler, a small piece of sticky tape, press fasteners, needle and grey cotton.

For the choker cut silver foil or cellophane into approximately 37 pieces (more or less, according to neck size), each 5cm by 10cm (2ins by 4ins).

Fold in half lengthways, then fold once more; then fold in half widthways.

With two pieces slide one piece up into the middle of the other, as shown in the illustration. Continue in this way, putting one up and one down for the length required. Seal tightly as you go by folding back behind each open end of the previous piece.

Make a continuous circle. Stitch with press fasteners at the ends. A matching dress button can be stitched on the outside, if desired. Seal along the inside with a strip of sticky tape.

For a bracelet to match, make approximately 16 pieces for an average wrist. Make as for the choker.

Finished effect

A matching belt requires wider pieces, 13cm by 8cm (5ins by 3ins). Make long enough to fit waist. Finish as before, or insert finished ends through a buckle with open centre, and stitch at the back.

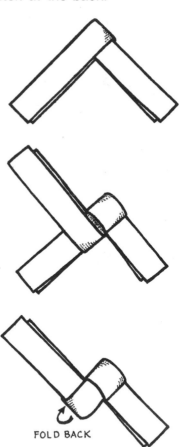

FOLD BACK

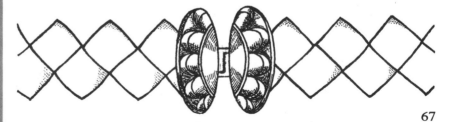

No Camp for Caroline

by Jo Picton

"Will you be able to come to camp with us this year, Caroline?"

"Oh, yes, Mrs Leach. Mum says it's all right, and I'm saving hard. I do odd jobs for people on Saturdays, like shopping and taking children out, and I cut Mrs Hill's lawn for her and weed her garden. She pays me."

The Guider smiled down at the small Guide. She knew how hard it was for Mrs Lane to bring up her family. Her husband had been killed when the lorry he was driving skidded on a wet road.

"I'm so glad, Caroline. We are going to Barnleigh and we always have a wonderful time there."

Caroline ran home, her eyes shining. She had never been to camp, but the other girls in her Patrol told her wonderful stories of camp-life. As she passed Mr Holt's gate she stopped to pat Punch, a beautiful golden-and-white collie.

"Hello, Caroline!" called the old man. "Are you coming to help me bath Punch on Saturday? It's getting too much for me now. He's very lively, and it takes me all my time to keep him groomed."

Caroline hugged the dog. "He always looks perfect to me, Mr Holt. I wish he was mine. I'd love a dog, but Mum says she has enough to feed as it is."

Punch and Caroline were great friends. Every morning on her way to school Caroline stopped to speak to him, and on fine days she took him for a walk after school. "It's almost like having a dog of my own, isn't it, Punch," she said as they romped together, "though not quite."

Easter was quite warm. The Guides went for hikes over the moors. Caroline loved cooking out of doors. She learnt to make a trench-fire and how to cook in tinfoil and red-hot ash.

"Is camp like this?" she asked her Patrol Leader.

"Camp? It's a hundred times better than this," was the enthusiastic reply.

Caroline took Punch for long walks. When they got back to the cottage there was always delicious soup or a cup of cocoa and a cake for her and a bone for Punch. Mr Holt often slipped a tenpenny piece into her hand as she left. He knew she was saving up for camp.

"But I don't want to be paid," Caroline protested. "You know how I love taking Punch out." But the old man just smiled.

The warm weather ended. It rained for days on end, and, to make things worse for Caroline, she became ill. It was more than a fortnight before she could go back to school.

"I hope Punch will remember me," she thought, as she ran down the road to Mr Holt's house, but there was no dog waiting for her at the gate.

"Oh, dear, he's forgotten!" she said as she looked eagerly over the gate.

Finally, she walked up to Mr Holt's front door and knocked. The place was very quiet. Why didn't Punch bark?

"Were you looking for Mr Holt, my dear?" called the lady from the cottage next door. "The old chap died about three weeks ago. They took him off to hospital."

"Oh, I am sorry!" cried Caroline. "What happened to Punch?" she asked.

"The police took him. Wouldn't leave the house, he wouldn't. They didn't half have a job getting him away. Real nasty, that dog was."

Tears came into Caroline's eyes. She was very fond of Mr Holt, and she was deeply troubled about Punch. What had happened to him? Calling over the hedge, she thanked the next-door neighbour and ran quickly out of the gate. She knew where the police-station was; she had learnt that at Guides.

"What can I do for you, my dear?" asked a smiling policeman at the station.

"Please can you tell me what has happened to Punch, old Mr. Holt's dog? The lady next door said that you took him away."

"Yes, we did, and a fine job we had moving him. He wouldn't leave the house. Broke the lead

"The old chap died three weeks ago," Caroline was told

see Punch? He's a golden-and-white collie. He belonged to Mr Holt."

The young man looked sad. "Yes, but I don't think the poor chap is long for this world. He won't eat, and he snaps if we try

"Of course he knows me . . . he's almost my dog. Can I go in to him?"

"Yes, and would you try to feed him? We are really worried about him."

"Of course I will. Give me his

"That can't be Punch!" cried Caroline

twice and ran back home before we got him here. He's at the pet shop in Adam Street. The old man's nephew said he has to be sold. He's a hard one, that man. He sold all the old man's treasures and the cottage; said he had no room for the rubbish. He said the dog was worth money and he'd have to be sold."

"Thank you very much."

With a heavy heart, Caroline turned away. She made her way to Adam Street. She found the shop easily. A young man with a kind face came forward as she entered.

"Please," she said, "could I

to go near him. He tries to get out all the time. The owner wants to sell him, but there isn't a hope as far as I can see; no one will want that bag of bones."

"Bag of bones?" Caroline was horrified. Punch was no bag of bones.

They walked out into a yard, where runs for the animals were situated around the walls.

"There he is, over in the corner," said the young man.

"No! That can't be Punch!" Caroline looked at the dog huddled in the corner of the run. His coat was matted, his eyes dull. "Punch! Oh, Punch darling!" she called.

The dog jumped up, barking wildly and wagging his tail.

"He knows you, miss."

dish." Caroline stooped down and talked quietly to Punch through the wire, and when the young man came back with a dish of meat and biscuits she went in. Punch almost knocked her down in his excitement.

"Come on, Punch; eat your dinner like a good dog." She held out the dish, and the dog wolfed down the meat.

"Well, I'm blowed!" said the young man. "He certainly knows you, and seems to love you."

Caroline stayed with Punch for some time, but then had to go back into the shop. She could hear Punch yelping, but she did not turn back.

"How much do you want for him?" she asked the young man.

"Well!" The young man rubbed his nose thoughtfully. "First of all the owner wanted ten pounds, but now he'll take five. Actually, the dog is worth a lot more, but he's pining away, and the owner will take what he can get for him."

Caroline thought quickly. There was her camp money, but so far that only amounted to three pounds and fifty pence.

"I only have three pounds, fifty," she said, "but I'd work for the rest—that is, if my mother will let me have him."

"I hope she will. We'll soon have to bury him if you don't take him. Perhaps we could split the difference as he's in such poor shape."

"I'll run all the way home and ask Mum."

Before the young man could answer, Caroline shot out of the shop. She arrived home breathless, her hair falling over her face. Her mother was out in the kitchen as she burst in. "Oh, *please*, Mummy, let me have Punch. If you could only see him I know you would."

"Now, what's all this? Take it quietly, Caroline." Her mother rubbed her hands down her apron.

Caroline told the story, tears running down her cheeks. "Mummy, Punch will die if we don't have him; I know he will. I'll pay for him."

"And what about camp? And who will pay for his food?" asked her mother.

Caroline gulped back a sob. "I can go to camp next year," she said, her voice trembling a little. "I'll keep on doing odd jobs to pay for Punch's food."

"Bless you, Caroline! Yes, you shall have your dog. I'll be glad to have him too; there's been a lot of burglaries around here lately and it will be good to have a dog to protect us."

Caroline rushed upstairs for the tin where she kept her camp money, and was soon back at the pet shop.

Men don't cry, but there was something queer about the young man's eyes as he counted out the small cash in the tin.

"Thank you very much," he said. "I'm very glad Punch will have a good home. Tell you what: I could do with some help on a Saturday morning. Would you come?"

"Would I?" Caroline was speechless. Then: "Yes, please —thank you!"

There was no camp for Caroline that year, but any evening a beautiful golden-and-white collie dog and a happy girl could be seen running over the common together.

There was something queer about the man's eyes as he counted the cash

Hiking and Cooking Hints

by Ann M. Stephenson

Hike Cooks

Every Guide knows the theory of hiking and hike-cooking, but the only real teacher is experience. These few hints have been written from an exclusively practical point of view, unorthodox though some of them may seem.

What happens on some hikes? It rains; the fire won't light; when it does light you run out of wood, and after an hour or so you find yourself staring at a half-cooked dinner and a pile of rapidly cooling sticks. Everybody is hungry and fed-up and you wish that you had never suggested the beastly hike in the first place.

Plan It All!

Proper planning can avoid most of the common pitfalls, so, several days before you go, sort out with your Patrol where you are going to go, and when. In the heat of summer, an evening picnic with supper is often more fun than a mid-day hike. If you cannot read a map with confidence, choose a simple route, preferably on a clearly marked footpath. Decide where you are going to stop for your meal, and, if it is on private land and you want to light a fire, get the permission of the landowner first. If you live by the sea, it is often possible to build your fire on the beach, but be sure that you are not causing inconvenience to other people. Remember, a Guide shows consideration for others! It is a good idea to have an alternative route in case it rains on the day; let it end up at somebody's house where you can do your cooking indoors.

The next thing is to sort out your menu. There are two ways of doing this. Either everybody chips-in to the cost of a common meal, or, better still, every girl is made responsible for providing her own food. This method does save the moans of "Oh, I never eat this!" or "I can't eat that," but it is sometimes necessary to advise members of the Patrol as to the right foods to take. Keep your menu simple, with only one or two cooked dishes. It is a good idea to take along as well something that does not need cooking, such as a sandwich. Disasters do occur, and this will at least mean that you do not go hungry. A good specimen menu is:

> Soup (only if you want to take a billy), pork chops (cooked in foil), fresh tomatoes, cheese sandwich, "s'mores", apples.
>
> The recipe for "s'mores" is as follows: for one "s'more": 2 plain digestive biscuits, 4 squares of chocolate, a marshmallow.
>
> Toast the marshmallow on a stick until it is nearly liquid. Place two squares of chocolate on one of the biscuits. Put the toasted marshmallow on top. Put the remaining two squares of chocolate on top of the marshmallow. Put the other biscuit on top. Press gently so that it all sticks together.
>
> The equipment needed for this meal will be one billycan, plenty of aluminium foil, water, washing-up liquid and cloth, drying-cloth, knife.

You'll Need These

You will also need to take a penknife, a map, first-aid kit, matches, a tin-opener, and a "punk-box". Be sure you take a tin-opener that somone knows how to use. The "punk-box", full of miscellaneous inflammable material, is an old Guiding institution. "Punk" consists of bits of dry birch-bark, pine-needles, tiny twigs, crumbled candle-wax, and, un-Guide-like but best of all, a chopped-up firelighter. Using a chunk of firelighter may not be in the spirit of B.-P., but it certainly gets your fire going, especially if the wood is damp! If there is room in your haversack, take a small bundle of perfectly dry wood with you, to give your fire a good start. Now everything is ready. All you need is a fine day. This, of course, can't be guaranteed, but Guides are trained to adapt to conditions.

Burning Questions

When you reach the place where you intend to cook your meal, stop and think before you light your fire. If you are on peat-moor, don't. Use a spirit-stove, or go without. Peat burns, and even though you may think your fire is out it only needs a tiny piece of still-smouldering peat to go on burning down to make a full-scale heath-fire break out later. If you are on a beach or in a wood, do NOT light your fire up against a sand-dune or a tree. Fire will scorch the roots of the grass that holds the dune together, and will seriously damage, if not kill, a growing tree. Never light a fire where there is any danger of its spreading or causing any damage to anything.

While some of the Patrol collect wood, clear a space for your fire, by turfing if necessary. Cut the turf deep and as cleanly as possible; it is often easier to cut the turf into four pieces, and lay it carefully down, well away from the fire. Do not light your fire until you have a suitably large woodpile. There is nothing worse than getting a fire going just nicely, only to run out of wood. Build your fire in the shape of a wigwam, and once it gets going lay a log (preferably at least 5cm (2") thick) on either side of the fire. This helps create a through-draught, keeps the fire together, and gives you something to rest your pans on. Do not make a fireplace of smooth stones or of flints; if they get hot, they are liable to explode. In fact,

Photographs: Miss J. Samman and Mrs A. Francis

be over-cautious and do not make a fireplace of any type of stone, rough or smooth.

Concentrate on getting a really good fire going before you start cooking; the best cooking-fire is one with a good bed of red-hot embers. The type of fire to aim for is one that will go on burning even if it is raining. It need not be large, just hot. Any wood except elder will do for a fire, although poplar is rather smoky. Oak, ash and beech, along with silver birch, are the best woods, but it is unusual to find them in great profusion near your fire-site. I personally have cooked over fires of cypress and rhododendron wood, and still managed to get meals cooked. Never strip growing branches from a tree; they will not burn well and only injure the tree. Nor should you cut birch-bark off a growing tree. If you cut the bark off in a strip all the way round the tree you will kill it. Damp, rotten wood is best kept until the fire is hot enough to dry it out. Put damp sticks at the edge of the fire, and, once they are dry, they can be used. Try to keep your fire compact; it will do less damage to the surrounding grass.

Once your fire has a good bed of glowing embers and is nice and hot, start cooking. Wrap each chop completely in foil and put it in the embers. It will take at least twenty minutes to cook, probably more, depending on the state of your fire. Cook it until it looks done when you unwrap a corner. If in doubt, aim to over-cook it.

If you are having soup, put it on about five minutes before you expect to eat it. Before you do anything, though, cover the OUTSIDE (NOT the inside) of the billy with a layer of washing-up liquid. If you do this, the fire-

blackening will wash straight off and thus save hours of work with steel wool. When you put the soup on to heat, put the empty tin straight into the fire, unless there is a litter-bin handy. "Burning and bashing" tins is a hygenic and neat method of rubbish disposal.

As soon as you have served the soup, fill the billy with water and put it back on the fire. It is not necessary to do this on the beach, where you can wash out the billy in the sea and scour it with sand. Eat your first course before starting to cook the next one, particularly in the case of "s'mores". If you make "s'mores" in advance, the marshmallow gets every-where!

Leave Only Thanks

Once you've finished eating, it is time to clear up. Scraps and rubbish should have been burned, the fire being kept burning for this express purpose. Take the billy off the fire, pour some cold water in with the hot,

and clean it thoroughly inside and out. Flatten the burned tin by stamping on it, then, when all rubbish has been burned, put the fire out with the washing-up water. Take out all the half-burned sticks, and dig a hole under the the ashes to bury the tin and the foil. Stamp the ashes and earth down firmly, and replace the turf neatly. Pour any remaining water over the turf, and put any left-over wood neatly under a hedge. Disposal of any-thing should be as unobtrusive as possible. It should be genuine disposal, not simply a matter of stuffing the rubbish down a con-venient rabbit-hole! Take a last look round before you go. The only signs of your sojourn should be a little trampled grass and a neatly replaced square of turf—no apple-cores, cans, can-rings or scraps of paper! Then, and only then, can you continue on your way, feeling that you will really be able to write in your Patrol logbook: EXPEDI-TION SUCCESSFUL.

Which way?

Where Am I?

Asks George H. Haines

If you are out and become lost, here are some hints that will help you find which direction is North

1. Hold your watch so that the hour-hand points to the sun. A line midway between the hour hand and the figure 12 points South. During the operation of BST take a line midway between the hour-hand and the figure 1 on your watch.

2. The arms of a weather vane indicate N E S and W.

3. Most old churches are built so that the altar is at the east end.

4. A horizontal sundial is set so that its gnomon (or pointer) slopes to the south. If you see a tilted dial like the one photographed (it is called an equinoctial dial) the raised end points S.

5. On old trees the side most likely to have moss on it is that facing north.

6. If you have a map, you can set it by lining it up so that it points to two features you can identify—such as a castle, a church or a distant hill.

Answers to Puzzles and Quizzes

Countryside Quiz (pages 16 and 17)
1. The vane. 2. Yes. The sharp spikes at the crown might accumulate in the stomach. 3. The eggs or roe of the sturgeon fish. 4. Spruce is the Christmas tree. 5. Frogs. 6. "Clear moon, frost soon." 7. Robin, great-tit or bluetit. 8. A butterfly. 9. Geese. 10. True. 11. Doe. 12. The isle of Fetlar, Shetland. 13. The thrush family. 14. Albumen. 15. Three—the grass snake, the smooth snake, and the adder or viper. 16. An exultation of larks. 17. A fish. 18. Venison. 19. Barn owl. 20. One who studies birds. 21. Green woodpecker. 22. "As bald as a coot." 23. Salmon family. 24. Rook and jackdaw. 25. A horse or pony. 26. "Red sky at morning, shepherd's warning." 27. Yorkshire. 28. Stickleback. 29. Fungi. 30. Lochs. 31. It's a sheepfold, and it is used for separating sheep where several farmers share the same ground. 32. Great skua. 33. Packhorse bridge. 34. The curlew. 35. To prevent their escape through fences on to roads. 36. A silhouette.

Stitch Puzzle (p. 19)
Across
1—Stem, 4—Chain, 7—Blanket, 8—Cross, 9—Running. *Down* 2—Tacking, 3—Bone, 5—Fly, 6—Herring

Catch Crossword (p. 19)
Answer: QUIET

Which Badges? (p. 19)
1. Jane—Friend to the Deaf; Mary—Pathfinder; Sue—Interpreter.
2. Anne—Stitchery; Sarah—Commonwealth Knowledge; Elizabeth—Health.
3. Jill—Bird Watcher; Carol—Poultry Farmer; Tonya—Observer.
4. Mandy—Handywoman; Polly—Farmer; Diana—Artist

Pioneering Puzzle (p. 22)
1—Figure-of-eight, 2—Timber, 3—Reef, 4—Fraying, 5—Granny, 6—Yarn, 7—Nylon, 8—Natural, 9—Loop, 10—Pickets, 11—Shroud-laid, 12—Double, 13—Elastic, 14—Cylindrical, 15—Ladders, 16—Spanish

Countryside Creatures (p. 23)
BIRDS: 1. *Robin:* gardens, woods, parks. 2. *Herring-gull:* seashore, cliffs. 3. *Heron:* rivers, lakes. 4. *Peewit (Lapwing):* farmland, coastal waters. 5. *Bluetit:* woods, orchards, gardens. 6. *Wren:* almost anywhere on land, not in cities. 7. *Swallow:* inside farm buildings, outhouses, etc. 8. *House-martin:* under house-eaves. 9. *Woodpecker:* timbered land, woods. 10. *Pheasant:* woodland, commons, heaths. 11. *Kingfisher:* rivers, canals, lakes. 12. *Cormorant:* seacoasts.
ANIMALS: 1. *Fox:* earth (fields, woods). 2. *Otter:* holt (waterways). 3. *Mole:* nest (gardens, fields). 4. *Stoat:* burrow (fields). 5. *Hare:* form (fields). 6. *Badger:* sett (woods). 7. *Squirrel:* drey (trees). 8. *Dormouse:* nest (woodlands). 9. *Weasel:* nest (fields). 10. *Rabbit:* burrow (woods, fields).

Puzzlewords—1 (p. 30)
Puzzlewords—2 (p. 30)

Pig Crossword (p. 30)

Mousy Masterpieces (p. 49)
1: Napoleon by Davide

Track the Blackbirds (pages 56, 57)
The trail is shown by the letters of the word ORIENTEERING

Mountain Crossword Puzzle (p. 62)

Badge Jigsaw (p. 62)
Artist

"Now does it feel more like home?"

Fun in the Dark
by Jean Howard

Make a chart showing the phases of the moon so that you can plan some activities for bright moonlight nights and for very dark ones.

After the moon, the stars! It takes time to recognise all the major stars and constellations, but you can quickly learn to identify Orion's Belt, Cassiopaea, the Plough, etc. Plot them with little gold or silver stars on a large circular sheet of dark-blue paper and gradually add more, making sure that all the Patrol can find them in the sky. Then go out with the Patrol and plot a compass course using the North Star as a guide. You will find this quite exciting; lives have been saved by people knowing how to navigate by the stars.

An interesting game for a very dark night is to tie a rope between two trees or posts. Tie or peg an article—anything you like—on the rope every few feet and leave it hanging. Each

member of the Patrol takes it in turn to feel her way along the rope and tries to identify each article by touch or smell or sound. Returning, she reports or writes down what she thinks each article is. This game can be played indoors too—in darkness, of course!

For a moonlight night plan an inter-Patrol or joint Guide/Scout incident course. Over a journey of a few miles arrange a number of incidents—like making a rope-ladder, putting up an improvised flagstaff, crossing a simu-

Blindfolded Guides follow a string trail. On a dark night try identifying objects hung or pegged on a string tied between two trees

lated "ravine", putting up a lightweight tent, or judging the height of a church-tower. End up with hot soup and sausages round a camp-fire.

Finally, a night hike—perhaps during camp. Your Guiders or Patrol Leaders take a number of Guides equipped with compasses and a torch (for reading maps) over a course of five or six miles. During the hike try to identify trees by the feel of the bark or the shape or smell of leaves, twigs, berries and flowers. Listen for bird calls and the movements of creatures searching for their supper, and watch the lights of night-flying planes and try to judge what compass course they are on. End up, of course, if at camp, with a meal!

These Guides show their skill at lashing on a Backwoodsman and Pioneer course. On an incident course at night could you make a rope-ladder or put up a flagstaff or a lightweight tent?